Scholastic Success With

GRADE 2
WORKBOOK

Scholastic Canada Ltd.

Toronto New York London Auckland Sydney
Mexico City New Delhi Hong Kong Buenos Aires

Scholastic Canada Ltd.
604 King Street West, Toronto, Ontario M5V 1E1, Canada

Scholastic Inc.
557 Broadway, New York, NY 10012, USA

Scholastic Australia Pty Limited
PO Box 579, Gosford, NSW 2250, Australia

Scholastic New Zealand Limited
Private Bag 94407, Botany, Manukau 2163, New Zealand

Scholastic Children's Books
Euston House, 24 Eversholt Street, London NW1 1DB, UK

www.scholastic.ca

Maps workbook copyright © 2002 by Linda Ward Beech

Cover art by Rob McClurkan
Interior illustrations by Jon Buller, Reggie Holladay, Anne Kennedy, Bob Masheris,
Mark Mason, and Carol Tiernon
Interior design by Quack & Company

ISBN 978-1-4431-6345-3

7 6 5 4 3 2   Printed in Canada 118   20 21 22 23 24

Table of Contents

WRITING

MAPS

ADDITION & SUBTRACTION

MATH

"Nothing succeeds like success."

Alexandre Dumas the Elder, 1854

Dear Parent,

Congratulations on choosing this excellent educational resource for your child. Scholastic has long been a leader in educational publishing—creating quality educational materials for use in school and at home for nearly a century.

As a partner in your child's academic success, you'll want to get the most out of the learning experience offered in this book. To help your child learn at home, try following these helpful hints:

- ✣ Provide a comfortable place to work.

- ✣ Have frequent work sessions, but keep them short.

- ✣ Praise your child's successes and encourage his or her efforts. Offer positive help when a child makes a mistake.

- ✣ Display your child's work and share his or her progress with family and friends.

In this workbook you'll find hundreds of practise pages that keep kids challenged and excited as they strengthen their skills across the classroom curriculum.

The workbook is divided into eight sections: Reading Comprehension; Reading Tests; Contemporary Manuscript; Grammar; Writing; Maps; Addition and Subtraction; and Math. You and your child should feel free to move through the pages in any way you wish.

The table of contents lists the activities and the skills practised. And a complete answer key in the back will help you gauge your child's progress.

Take the lead and help your child succeed with the *Scholastic Success With: Grade 2 Workbook!*

The activities in this workbook reinforce age-appropriate skills and will help your child meet the following standards established as goals by leading educators.

Mathematics

★ Uses a variety of strategies when problem-solving

★ Understands and applies number concepts

★ Uses basic and advanced procedures while performing computation

★ Understands and applies concepts of measurement

★ Understands and applies concepts of geometry

Writing

★ Understands and uses the writing process

★ Uses grammatical and mechanical conventions in written compositions

Reading

★ Understands and uses the general skills and strategies of the reading process

★ Can read and understand a variety of literary texts

★ Can understand and interpret a variety of informational texts

Geography

★ Understands the characteristics and uses of maps and globes

★ Knows the location of places, geographic features, and patterns of the environment

Scholastic Success With

READING
COMPREHENSION

Try This!

*When you are reading, do you get stuck on words that you don't know? Does not knowing a word make it hard to understand what you are reading? This idea can help you. Use **context clues** to figure out what the word is. That means think about the other words in the sentence. What clues do they give? Then ask yourself what other word would make sense there.*

What do you think the underlined word means in each sentence below? Circle the meaning that makes sense. Then rewrite each sentence using the meaning instead of the underlined word.

1. My domino has two white <u>pips</u>, and yours has five.

    baby dogs   spots   long metal tubes

    _____

2. A grey <u>fulmar</u> flew by the cruise ship.

    lizard   swordfish   seabird

    _____

    _____

3. The queen had a beautiful necklace made of <u>jasper</u>.

    a green stone   yellow pudding   wet snow

    _____

4. My sister is the best <u>flutist</u> in the high school band.

    waitress   runner   flute player

    _____

 Write a meaning for this nonsense word: zeebit. Use it in a sentence on another piece of paper. See if a friend can guess the meaning of your word by looking at the clues in the sentence.

Moon Walk

 *The **main idea** tells what the whole story is about.*

Neil Armstrong was an astronaut. He made history on July 20, 1969. He was the first man to walk on the moon! When he stepped on the moon, he said, "That's one small step for (a) man, one giant leap for mankind." Millions of people were watching this amazing event on TV. It was an awesome thing to look up at the moon that night and know that a man was walking around on it! For years, people had wondered if there would be moon creatures living there. But the only things Armstrong found were moon rocks and moon dust.

Draw a line connecting the correct star words that tell the main idea of the story. Begin at Earth. Some star words will not be used.

uncle   dance   walk   moon

                    to

          river   on

                 cold   uncle

Armstrong   man   the

       was   frog

Neil   hat

           the   candy

                                plate
              first

Write a short story with this title: "My Trip to the Moon." Underline the main idea of the story.

ABC

 *The **main idea** of a story tells what the whole story is about.*

When you were in kindergarten, or maybe before that, you learned your ABCs. Letters are the building blocks for words. Words are the building blocks for sentences. We use sentences to communicate our thoughts and feelings. Each letter of the alphabet has at least one sound. Some letters have more than one sound. There are 26 letters in our alphabet. Many of our letters came from alphabets made many years ago in foreign countries. In fact, the word *alphabet* comes from two words, *alpha* and *beta*, which are the first two letters in the Greek alphabet!

Underline the title that describes the main idea of this story.

Playing With Blocks   **All About Our Alphabet**   **The Greek Language**

Now let's play a game using the alphabet. Read each clue below. Draw a line to the letters that sound like the correct answer.

1. I borrowed some money from your piggy bank. _____ fifty cents.

2. That fall did not hurt me. I'm _____.

3. What did the blind man say to the doctor who made him see again? _____

4. What insect makes honey? _____

5. I drank all my milk. Now my glass is _____.

6. What kind of plant is that? _____

ICU

MT

OK

AB

IOU

IV

Call the Police!

It is good to know that you can call a police officer when you need help. You should not be afraid of the police. Their job is to help people. Police officers help find lost children. They direct traffic when there is a problem on the roads. They arrest criminals so that our towns are safe. When people have been in car accidents, police officers come quickly to help them. During floods, fires, and tornadoes, they take people to safe places. Sometimes they rescue people who are in danger. Police officers have saved many lives. Think of a police officer as your best friend!

What do you think the main idea of this story is? To find out, read the letters that are connected in the puzzle. Write the letters in order beside the matching shapes.

 Write a letter to your town's police officers. Make sure the letter's main idea is to thank them for keeping your town safe. Ask an adult to mail it for you.

Rachel's Recipe

 Details *are parts of a story. Details help you understand what the story is about.*

On Saturday, Rachel got up early. Her mom was still asleep, so Rachel made her own breakfast. She put some peanut butter in a bowl. She mixed it with a little honey. Then she stirred in some oatmeal, bran flakes, and raisins. It tasted yummy! When Mom got up, she said, "Oh! You made granola!"

Follow the directions below.

- Circle the word that tells who the main character is.

- Underline the word that tells what day Rachel made breakfast.

- Put a box around the word that tells what dish Rachel put the peanut butter in.

- Put a star by each of the four words that tell what she mixed with the peanut butter.

- Put a dotted line under the word that describes how it tasted.

- Put two lines under the word that tells what Mom called the food.

Now find each of the nine words in the puzzle below and circle it. The words go across and down.

B	R	A	N	F	L	A	K	E	S	M	H	N	C	L
O	A	T	M	E	A	L	B	K	E	Q	O	J	W	I
W	R	A	I	S	I	N	S	G	R	A	N	O	L	A
L	G	S	A	T	U	R	D	A	Y	P	E	R	D	R
G	R	A	C	H	E	L	Y	U	M	M	Y	F	A	H

 On another sheet of paper, draw your favourite breakfast. Then write the steps to prepare it.

Rodeo Clowns

 Details *are parts of a story. Details help you understand what the story is about.*

Have you ever been to a rodeo or seen one on TV? If so, you probably saw some rodeo clowns. Like clowns at a circus, they entertain the audience by doing funny tricks to make people laugh. But the main job of rodeo clowns is to protect the cowboys from the bulls. They try to catch the bull's attention long enough to allow the cowboy to escape from the arena without getting hurt. Bulls are quite fast, and they make sudden moves, so it is hard to get away from them. Angry bulls use their horns as weapons. Rodeo clowns sometimes jump in a barrel while the bull pushes it around. Other times they wave their arms or yell to keep the bull away from the cowboy. They make it look like a funny game, but it is really a very dangerous job.

Circle the letter under true or false to show your answer.

True	False	
B	Z	1. Rodeo clowns do funny tricks.
R	U	2. Rodeo clowns work at the circus.
L	M	3. Rodeo clowns help protect the cowboys.
A	L	4. Rodeo clowns distract the goats while the cowboy gets away.
R	X	5. Rodeo clowns are brave.
I	V	6. Bulls can make sudden moves.
F	D	7. Bulls use their tails as weapons.
P	E	8. Sometimes rodeo clowns jump in a cardboard box while the bull pushes it around.
R	W	9. Sometimes rodeo clowns yell and wave their arms to distract the bulls.
S	C	10. Rodeo clowns have a very dangerous job.

To find out who likes rodeo clowns, write the letters you circled in order.

___ ___ ___ ___ ___ ___ ___ ___ ___ ___

Gorillas

 Details *are parts of a story. Details help you understand what the story is about.*

Gorillas are the largest apes. They live in the rain forests of Africa. Every morning, they wake up and eat a breakfast of leaves, fruit, and bark. During most of the day, the adult gorillas take naps. Meanwhile, young gorillas play. They wrestle and chase each other. They swing on vines. When the adults wake up, everyone eats again. When there is danger, gorillas stand up on their hind legs, scream, and beat their chests. Every night before it gets dark, the gorillas build a new nest to sleep in. They break off leafy branches to make their beds, either on the ground or in the trees. Baby gorillas snuggle up to their mothers to sleep.

Find the answers to the puzzle in the story. Write the answers in the squares with the matching numbers.

Across

1. During the day, adult gorillas _____.

3. Gorillas eat leaves, bark, and _____.

5. The largest apes are _____.

7. In danger, gorillas beat their _____.

8. Young gorillas swing on _____.

Down

2. The continent where gorillas live is _____.

4. When young gorillas play, they _____ and chase each other.

6. Baby gorillas snuggle up to their mothers to _____.

 On another piece of paper, write two things gorillas do that people also do.

Fun at the Farm

Story events that can really happen are **real**. *Story events that are make-believe are* **fantasy**.

Read each sentence below. If it could be real, circle the picture. If it is make-believe, put an X on the picture.

 Dairy cows give milk.

 The farmer planted pizza and hamburgers.

 The pig said,"Let's go to the dance tonight!"

 The mouse ate the dinner table.

 The hay was stacked in the barn.

 The chickens laid golden eggs.

 The red tractor ran out of gas.

 The newborn calf walked with wobbly legs.

 The goat and the sheep got married by the big tree.

 Two crickets sang "Mary Had a Little Lamb."

 Horses sat on the couch and watched TV.

 Rain made the roads muddy.

 Four little ducks swam in the pond.

 The farmer's friend baked a pumpkin pie.

 On another sheet of paper, write one make-believe sentence about the farmer's house and one real sentence about it.

Grandma Hugfuzzy

Grandma Hugfuzzy lived all alone in the country. She loved to sit on the porch and watch the animals. Every day, she put food out for the rabbits and raccoons. She fed the birds with scraps of bread. She put corn out for the deer. One terrible, awful, dreadful day, Grandma Hugfuzzy's house burned down. Poor Grandma! She had nowhere to go and no one to help her. She spent the night in an old barn on a bed of hay, crying herself to sleep. During the night, the animals came to her rescue. Nine black bears chopped down some trees. A herd of deer carried the wood on their antlers. Dozens of raccoons and squirrels worked all night building a log cabin for Grandma. Birds flew above the house nailing on the roof. When morning came, Grandma Hugfuzzy was amazed to see what her animal friends had done! She threw a big party for them that lasted ten years!

Write a red *R* on things that are real. Write a purple *F* on things that are fantasy.

a woman feeding animals

deer that carry lumber

a grandmother living alone

sleeping on hay in a barn

animals building a log cabin

Home Sweet Home

a house burning down

bears chopping down trees

birds that can nail on a roof

crying that her house burned

a party that lasted ten years

WELCOME

The first part of this story could be real. Draw a big orange star at the place where the story changes to fantasy.

The Change Game

Each sentence below is make-believe. Change it!
Rewrite the sentence so that it is real.
Study the example.

The broom carried the dog to the moon.

The broom was kept in the closet.

1. **The newborn baby was bigger than a house.**

   _____

2. **The walls were painted with gooey green slime.**

   _____

3. **The mayor turned into a frog.**

   _____

Now change and do it the other way! Each sentence below is real.
Change it so that it is fantasy. Study the example.

The moon is made of rocks and ice.

The moon is made of green cheese.

4. **The black spider crawled across the floor.**

   _____

5. **The deep-sea diver saw a whale and five dolphins.**

   _____

6. **My pizza has pepperoni and olives on it.**

   _____

On another piece of paper, draw a picture about one of your fantasy sentences.

The Rescue

 Sequencing *means putting the events in a story in the order that they happened.*

Mia's black cat climbed to the top of a telephone pole and couldn't get down. "Come down, Spooky!" cried Mia. Mia thought hard. What could she do? She went across the street to ask Mr. Carson for help. He was a firefighter before he retired. "What's the matter, Mia?" asked Mr. Carson when he saw Mia's tears. "My cat is up on that pole, and I can't get her down!" Mr. Carson hugged Mia and said, "I'll call my buddies at the fire station. They will come and help." A few minutes later, Mia saw the fire truck coming. The firefighters parked near the pole and raised a long ladder to the top. A firefighter climbed the ladder and reached out for Spooky. Just then, Spooky jumped to a nearby tree limb, climbed down the tree, and ran into the backyard. Mia said, "Spooky! You naughty cat!" Mr. Carson and the firefighters laughed and laughed.

Read the sentences on the ladder. Number them in the order that they happen in the story.

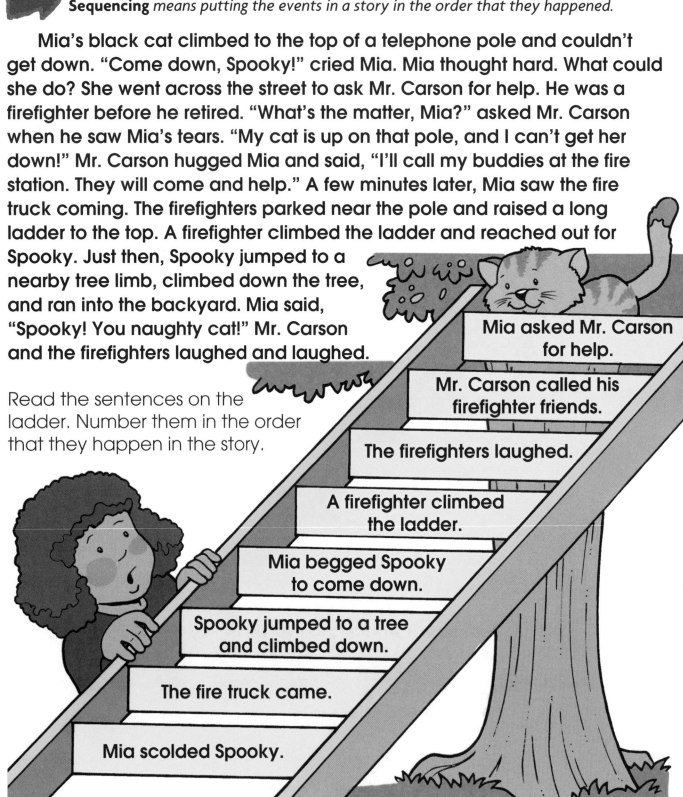

Mia asked Mr. Carson for help.

Mr. Carson called his firefighter friends.

The firefighters laughed.

A firefighter climbed the ladder.

Mia begged Spooky to come down.

Spooky jumped to a tree and climbed down.

The fire truck came.

Mia scolded Spooky.

New Kid in School

When they finished moving, Mom took Shelby to meet her new teacher. The teacher said, "Welcome to our school, Shelby. Let me tell you what we do in our Grade 2 class. We start the day with reading and writing. After that, we do math. Then we go out to recess. Just before lunch, we have social studies. We eat lunch at 11:00. Then we have story time. After story time, we have science. Then comes learning centres, where you can work on the computer, play a game, or read a book. Next, we have spelling. Finally, we go to music and art classes for the last hour of the day. Here is a schedule for you to take home. I'll see you tomorrow, Shelby!"

Fill in the blanks with the missing words or time.

Grade 2 Class Schedule

8:00	Reading and _____
9:00	_____
10:00	_____
10:30	_____
___:___	Lunch
11:30	_____
12:00	_____
1:00	Learning Centres
1:30	_____
2:00	_____ and Art
3:00	Go home.

A Pencil Sandwich?

How does the lead get inside a wooden pencil? Pencils are made out of strips of wood cut from cedar trees. Then grooves are cut in the strips. Graphite is laid into the grooves. (We call it lead, but it is really graphite.) Then another strip of wood is glued on top of the first one, making a pencil sandwich! The wood is rounded in rows on the top strip of wood and the bottom strip. Then the pencils are cut apart and painted. An eraser is added on the end and held in place by a metal ring. When you buy a pencil, you sharpen it, and then you are ready to write.

Look at the pictures. Number them in the order that they happen in the story.

□ graphite added

□ strips of wood

□ pencil sandwich

□ grooves

□ cut apart and painted

□ eraser added

□ rounded on top and bottom

□ sharpen

 Use a pencil to practise writing the alphabet, uppercase and lowercase.

Secret Message

Follow the directions in each shape. Write the answer in the shape that matches it. If you follow directions carefully, you will discover a secret message!

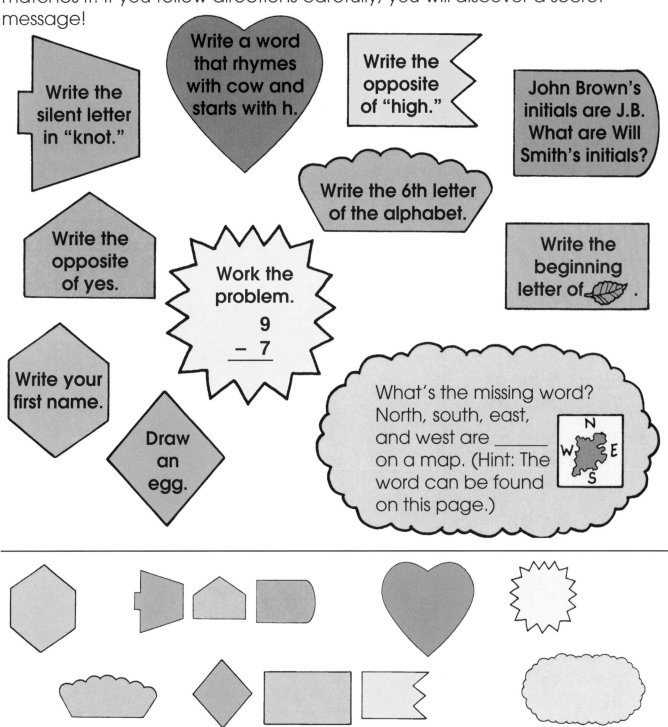

Write the silent letter in "knot."

Write a word that rhymes with cow and starts with h.

Write the opposite of "high."

John Brown's initials are J.B. What are Will Smith's initials?

Write the 6th letter of the alphabet.

Write the opposite of yes.

Work the problem.
9
– 7

Write the beginning letter of 🍃 .

Write your first name.

Draw an egg.

What's the missing word? North, south, east, and west are _____ on a map. (Hint: The word can be found on this page.)

 Write step-by-step directions that tell how to make a peanut butter and jelly sandwich.

Rainy Day Fun

One rainy afternoon, Jing and I decided to play grocery store. We went to the garage and set up four empty boxes for our shelves. Mom let us have all the canned food from the pantry to play with. We wrote prices on little strips of paper and taped them to the cans. We used Dad's calculator for our cash register. We set our cash register on the old table in the garage. Then we got some play money out of a game in my closet. Jing made signs that said, "Green Beans: 3 cans for $1.00" and things like that. There were lots of brown paper bags in the kitchen, so we took some to pack the groceries. When our cousins came over, we gave them some play money and let them be the customers. Then we traded places. Who cares if it rains when you are having so much fun?

Follow the directions to illustrate the story.

1. Draw a table and four empty boxes.

2. Draw cans in all the empty boxes.

3. Draw three signs on the wall telling what is being sold.

4. Draw Jing by the table.

5. Draw some play money in Jing's hand.

6. Draw two paper bags under the table.

Write the directions from your house to a another place in your neighbourhood. Follow the directions to see if they are correct.

After School at Jake's House

 *You are **drawing conclusions** when you use your own thoughts to answer the question, "How could that have happened?"*

Jake had a lot of homework to do. It was three pages long. He added and subtracted until his hand got tired of writing.

1. What kind of homework did Jake have?

   spelling   math   reading

What clues told you the answer? Underline them in the story.

After supper, Jake's dad reminded Jake to do his job. Jake went from room to room unloading baskets and cans into a large plastic bag. Then he took the bag out to the dumpster.

2. What was Jake's job?

   washing dishes   making the bed   taking out the trash

What clues told you the answer? Underline them in the story.

Now Jake could have some free time. He decided to play *Star Monsters*. He turned on the TV and put a cartridge in the player. He watched the monsters fighting on the TV screen while his fingers pushed buttons to make them move.

3. What was Jake doing?

   playing a video game   watching the news   playing with toys

What clues told you the answer? Underline them in the story.

Jake was tired. He put on his pajamas, brushed his teeth, and crawled under the covers.

4. What was Jake doing?

   waking up   getting ready for school   going to bed

What clues told you the answer? Underline them in the story.

?ti si tahW

Friday was a special day at my school. First of all, we wore our clothes differently. The back pockets of my jeans were in the front, and my shirt was buttoned up in the back. The teacher began the day with the subject we usually did last. All day, our schedule was opposite of what it usually was. We had to write our name backward on our papers. At lunch time, we ate dessert first, then our meals! When we went out to recess, we had to walk backward all the way to the playground. Then we had backward relay races. Some people fell down. Everyone was giggling! When it was time to go home, we sang "Good Morning to You."

1. What special day was it? Circle one.

   Valentine's Day   Grandparent's Day   Backward Day

2. Connect the dots in backward ABC order to find out how the teacher looked that day.

3. If the math assignment was to count by 5's to 50, how would the children have written it that day? Write the numbers.

Make up a spelling word list with ten words. Then write them the way the children would have written them on this special day.

They Could Do Better

Read each story below. Choose your answers from the bubble-gum machine. Write them on the lines.

bubble-gum machine containing: lying, told the truth, said "Excuse me", hurt his feelings, paid for it, helped him, showed bad manners, stealing

1. **When no one was looking, James took a piece of bubble gum from the candy counter and chewed it. Then he left the store.**

   What was James doing? _____

   What should he have done?

   _____

2. **Dad's boss, Mrs. Hill, came for dinner. Zach burped during the meal. He laughed. His dad looked angry.**

   What did Zach do wrong? _____

   What should he have done?_____

3. **While Mom was gone, Ashley played with matches. When Mom came home, she sniffed the air and said, "Ashley, did you light some matches?" Ashley said, "No, Mom, I didn't."**

   What was Ashley doing? _____

   What should she have done? _____

4. **Becky and Cindy saw a boy trip and fall down. Becky pointed at him and told Cindy to look. Then they laughed. The boy looked away sadly.**

   What did Becky and Cindy do?_____

   What should they have done? _____

💡 **On a piece of paper, write the name of a person in your class who has good manners. Explain why you came to that conclusion.**

Miss Maple

I am a maple tree. I live in Quebec. In the summer, my green leaves make a cool, shady place for people to rest. Every fall, my leaves turn brilliant colours of yellow, red, and orange. Some people think it looks like my leaves are on fire! In the winter, my leaves are all gone. I stretch my empty arms out to the falling snow. In the spring, little flowers appear along with my new leaves. That's when the sweet sap inside me begins to rise. People drill holes in my trunk and put a spout in me to drain the sap. Then they boil the sap and make maple syrup!

Add to and colour each picture the way it is described in the story.

Do you like maple syrup? Draw a picture of the kind of food that you would put maple syrup on.

Sentence Shapes

Let's have some fun reading and writing sentences! Look at the sentence below. It is shaped like what it is telling about.

Yahoo! I love rollercoasters. They are so much fun! They tickle my tummy!

Now it is your turn! Read each sentence below. Think about what it means. On another piece of paper, rewrite each sentence in the shape that shows what it is telling about. The shapes at the bottom of the page may help you.

1. I wonder if this box has my birthday gift in it.

2. I will send a valentine to someone that I love.

3. From space, the Earth looks like a blue marble.

4. If you see someone without a smile, give them one of yours.

5. Jets taxi down the runway, then fly into the air.

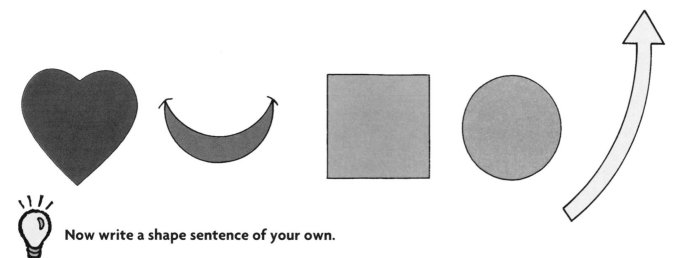

Now write a shape sentence of your own.

Curious Creature

Use story details to help you make decisions about what has happened in the story.

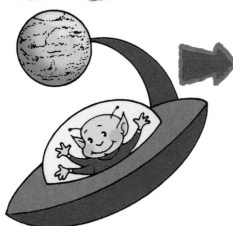

Zolak boarded his spaceship and blasted off from the planet Vartog. He was on a special mission to learn about earthlings. His spaceship landed gently in a desert. Zolak walked around looking for earthlings, but all he could see were rocks and sand. Then he looked down and saw a dark creature lying down right next to him. In fact, the creature's feet were touching Zolak's feet. Zolak was scared and tried to run away, but everywhere he went, the creature followed him. At noon, Zolak realized that the creature had shrunk to a very small size but was still right next to his feet. However, during the afternoon, the dark creature grew longer and longer! Then the strangest thing happened. Night came and the dark creature completely disappeared!

1. Who do you think the dark creature was? _____

2. Was the dark creature an earthling?   yes   no

3. Do you think Zolak will give a true report about the earthlings when he returns to Vartog?   yes   no

   Why or why not?

   _____

4. Draw a line to match the object to its correct shadow.

 On a piece of paper, write the story you think will appear in Vartog newspapers under the headline "Zolak Discovers a Curious Creature on Earth"

Figure It Out

Read each sentence. Then colour the numbered space in the picture that matches the number of the correct answer.

He rode his bike?
Who rode it?
 1. a boy
 2. a girl

Please bait my hook.
What am I doing?
 7. fishing
 8. playing baseball

Sorry! I broke it.
What could it be?
 13. a stuffed animal
 14. a crystal vase

Look at the dark cloud.
Where should you look?
 19. down
 20. up

The lamb lost its mother.
Who is its mother?
 21. a sheep
 22. a horse

She wore a red hat.
Who wore it?
 23. a man
 24. a woman

I see a thousand stars.
What time is it?
 25. noon
 26. night

Let's throw snowballs!
What time of year is it?
 3. summer
 4. winter

Breakfast is ready!
What time is it?
 9. night
 10. morning

He's a professor.
What is he?
 15. an adult
 16. a baby

Run, John, run!
What sport is John in?
 5. swimming
 6. track

I'm so thirsty.
What will I do?
 11. drink something
 12. eat something

It won't fit in the car.
What is it?
 17. a football
 18. a swing set

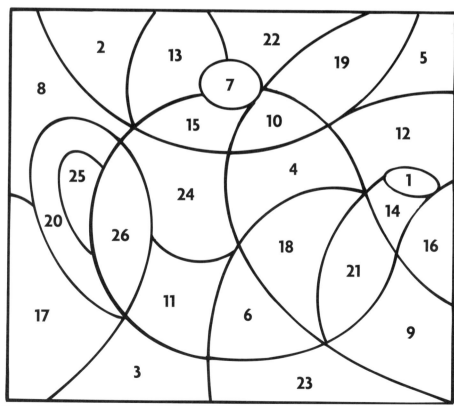

Riddle: What begins with T, ends with T, and has T in it? Find it in the puzzle.

Summer Vacation

Grouping like things together helps you see how parts of a story are connected and makes the story easier to understand.

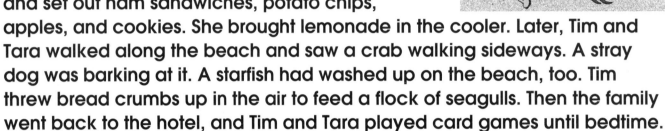

Last summer, Dad, Mom, Tim, and Tara went to the beach in Cape Breton. They swam, fished, built sandcastles, and went sailing. Mom brought a picnic lunch. She spread a blanket on the sand and set out ham sandwiches, potato chips, apples, and cookies. She brought lemonade in the cooler. Later, Tim and Tara walked along the beach and saw a crab walking sideways. A stray dog was barking at it. A starfish had washed up on the beach, too. Tim threw bread crumbs up in the air to feed a flock of seagulls. Then the family went back to the hotel, and Tim and Tara played card games until bedtime.

Use the story to find the answers. Fill in the blanks.

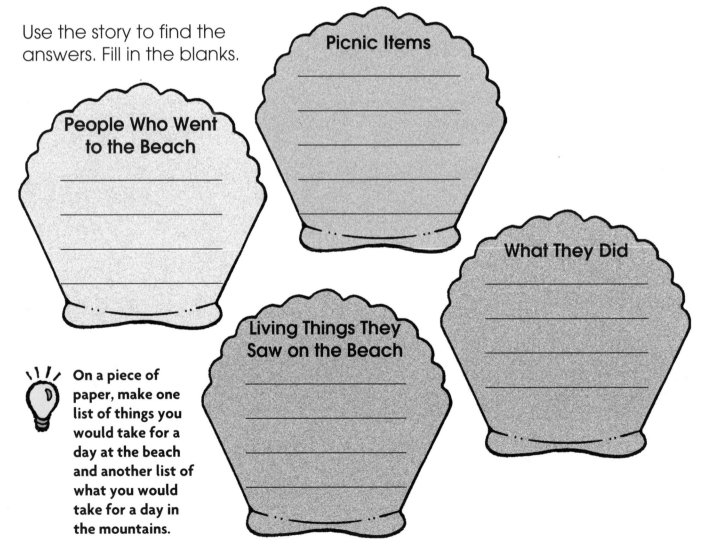

Picnic Items

_____

_____

_____

_____

People Who Went to the Beach

_____

_____

_____

_____

What They Did

_____

_____

_____

_____

Living Things They Saw on the Beach

_____

_____

_____

_____

On a piece of paper, make one list of things you would take for a day at the beach and another list of what you would take for a day in the mountains.

Which One Doesn't Belong?

 Look for similarities when grouping items.

Read each list. Cross out the word that doesn't belong. Then choose a word from the kite that belongs with each list and write it in the blank.

1. grouchy   mad   cheerful   fussy   _____

2. north   away   east   south   _____

3. goat   blue jay   robin   eagle   _____

4. juice   milk   tea   mud   _____

5. hand   toy   foot   head   _____

6. David   Lucas   Miguel   Sarah   _____

7. spinach   cake   cookies   pie   _____

8. glue   bicycle   pencils   scissors   _____

9. nickel   dime   quarter   marble   _____

arm
loonie
George
pudding
lemonade
parakeet
crayons
angry
west

Now read these categories. In each box, write the number from the above list that matches the category.

Birds	Desserts	Bad Feelings
Boys' Names	Money	School Supplies
Directions	Body Parts	Drinks

 Write a list of five things that go with this category: Things That Are Hot.

My Favourites

This page is all about you! Read the categories and write your own answers.

My Favourite TV Shows	My Favourite Foods	My Favourite Sports
_____	_____	_____
_____	_____	_____
_____	_____	_____

Draw two of your favourite people here and write their names.

Favourite Colour

_____

Favourite Holiday

_____

Favourite Song

_____

Favourite Movie

_____

Favourite School Subject

_____

Favourite Thing To Do After School

_____

Favourite Thing To Do With My Family

_____

Trade pages with friends and read what they wrote. You might get to know them a little better!

Name _____

Will He Be All Right?

➤ *Use story details to guess what will happen next.*

Father Eagle said to his young son, "Today is a very special day. You will fly for the first time." Baby Eagle was afraid. He said, "But Father, I don't know how. What should I do?" His father laid a strong wing on his little shoulder and said, "You will know." They stood at the edge of a very high cliff. Far below were huge rocks and a river. "Ride the wind, my son!" said Father Eagle, and he gently pushed his son off the cliff. Baby Eagle yelled, "Help! Help!" and wildly flapped his wings. All of a sudden something wonderful happened!

Help!

He got hurt.

He fell in the river.

He broke his wing on a tree limb.

He learned to fly.

1. What do you think happened next? Colour the rock that tells the most likely answer.

2. Why did you choose that answer? Find the sentence in the story that gives you a hint that the story has a happy ending. Write it here.

_____

_____

Unscramble the words and write the answer: **ODPRU**   **AARDFI**

3. How do you think Baby Eagle felt at first when he was pushed off

   the cliff? _____

4. How do you think Father Eagle felt at the end of the story? _____

What Will Happen Next?

Read each story. Write your answer on the blanks.

1. The baseball game was tied 6-6 at the bottom of the ninth inning with bases loaded. The home team batter hit a high fly ball deep into right field. The outfielder caught the ball but then dropped it. What will happen next?

_____

_____

_____

2. Adan decided to bake some brownies. He put them in the oven and went outside and jumped in the pool. He swam for a long time. He forgot all about the brownies. What will happen next?

_____

_____

_____

3. Mrs. Lopez ran over a big nail. It stuck in the tire. Air began to seep out. What will happen next?

_____

_____

_____

4. The wind began to blow. Dark clouds drifted in. Lightning cracked, and thunder roared. What will happen next?

_____

_____

_____

5. One day Greg left his toy truck on the stairs. Mom came down the stairs carrying a laundry basket, piled high with dirty towels. She stepped on Greg's truck. What will happen next?

_____

_____

_____

6. Dad and Olivia went fishing. They rowed the boat to the middle of the lake. Then they hit a rock that made a hole in the boat. Water started rushing in. What will happen next?

_____

_____

_____

 Choose one of the stories above and draw a picture of what happens next.

Wishes Come True

Once upon a time Rita Rabbit was complaining to Diana Duck. "You always have fun, swimming around in the lake. I wish I was a duck. You're lucky." Diana Duck said, "Oh, really? Well, I wish I was a rabbit! You can hop so fast and go so far. I think you're lucky!" Just then the Good Fairy appeared and said, "You are both lucky! I will grant you each your wish." All of a sudden Rita Rabbit became a duck! She waddled to the lake and went for a swim. Diana Duck became a rabbit and hopped down the road as fast as she could go. At the end of the day, Rita was wet and cold. She missed her family. She missed her home in the hole at the bottom of the hollow tree. She wanted to hop over there, but it was too far, and all she could do was waddle. Diana was having trouble, too. She had hopped so far away that she got lost. She began to cry. She wanted to go home to the lake. Just then . . . POOF! The Good Fairy appeared again. She granted Rita and Diana one more wish.

Draw what you think happened when Rita got her second wish.	Draw what you think happened when Diana got her second wish.

 If you had a wish, what would it be? On a piece of paper, draw a picture of what might happen if your wish came true.

Name _____

Zoo Reports

 Compare *means to look for things that are the same.*
Contrast *means to look for things that are different.*

The Grade 2 class went to the zoo for a field trip. The next day, the teacher asked the children to write a report about what they learned. Read the two reports below.

What I Learned at the Zoo by Ryan	What I Learned at the Zoo by Mariam
I learned about the giant tortoise. It was so big that the guide let us sit on its back. Some tortoises live to be over 100 years old! That's older than my grandpa! The slowest-moving mammal is the three-toed sloth. It hangs from trees and eats fruit. Some sloths sleep more than 20 hours a day. What a lazy animal! I thought the albino alligator was really cool. It wasn't green. It was completely white all over. It was born that way.	The tallest animal on earth is the giraffe. It eats leaves from the tops of the trees. Giraffes come from Africa. I learned about an albino alligator. It was white instead of green. The guide told us that it was born without the colouring of other alligators. I saw an owl sleeping in a tree. Owls sleep in the daytime and hunt at night. When they sleep, they don't fall out of the tree because they have sharp claws that lock onto the branch.

Ryan and Mariam each wrote about three animals. Write the names of the animals they wrote about in the correct circles. In the centre where both circles overlap, write the name of the animal that they both wrote about.

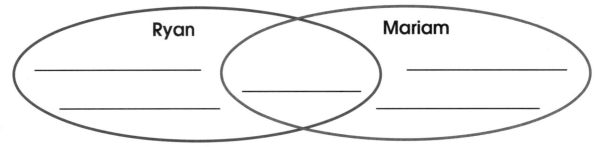

Ryan   Mariam

_____   _____   _____

_____   _____   _____

 Write three facts about a zoo animal. If you need help, use a dictionary or encyclopedia.

The Contest

The Super Grocery Store held a contest. Whoever could guess the correct number of jelly beans in the big jar would win a prize. There were exactly 372 jelly beans. Two people guessed the right answer. They were Joey Jumpjolly and Harry Honkhorn. Since there were two winners, each of them was given a $20 gift certificate. Joey Jumpjolly decided to spend his prize money on his favourite foods. He bought vanilla ice cream, animal cookies, angel food cake, and a chocolate candy bar. Harry Honkhorn had a different idea. He used his money to buy bacon, eggs, cereal, and waffles.

How are Joey and Harry alike? How are they different? To find out, work the puzzle below. Cross out all the *Q*'s, *V*'s, *Z*'s, and *X*'s. Next cross out all the numbers 1–9. Then cross out every question mark. What is left? Write the words in order in the blanks at the bottom of the page.

3	?	5	Q	B	O	T	H	9	9	7	X	H	A	D	6	2
T	W	E	N	T	Y	X	Q	8	D	O	L	L	A	R	S	7
X	V	5	Z	T	O	4	?	Q	S	P	E	N	D	3	2	1
?	Q	J	O	E	Y	3	B	O	U	G	H	T	Z	V	7	6
Z	9	X	S	W	E	E	T	S	4	?	V	H	A	R	R	Y
7	?	V	Z	V	B	O	U	G	H	T	8	9	X	V	3	7
B	R	E	A	K	F	A	S	T	4	?	V	F	O	O	D	X

_____   _____   _____   _____

_____   _____.   _____   _____

_____.   _____   _____

_____   _____.

On a piece of paper, make a list of what you would buy at a grocery store. Are your choices more like Joey's or Harry's?

The Accident

Kendra and her mom left their house on Oak Street to go to school. Kendra put on her seat belt. About that same time, Lacey and her mom left their house on Maple Street. On the way to school, Lacey bounced up and down on the seat watching her pigtails fly up and down in the mirror. She had forgotten to wear her seat belt. Both moms turned into the school parking lot at the same time, and they crashed into each other! Kendra was not hurt. Her seat belt kept her in her seat. But, Lacey fell forward and bumped her head HARD! She cried and cried. She had to go to the hospital and get an X-ray. Lacey got well in a day or two, but she learned an important lesson!

Draw a 😊 in the correct column.

	Kendra	Lacey	both
driven to school by Mom			
wore a seat belt			
didn't wear a seat belt			
lives on Maple Street			
was in a wreck			
bumped her head			
got an X-ray			
lives on Oak Street			
bounced up and down in the car			
didn't get hurt			
learned a lesson			

 Write a sentence telling why it is important to wear a seat belt.

What Is Cotton?

Cotton is a very useful plant. Farmers plant cotton in the spring. The plants grow and make white <u>flowers</u>. When a flower falls off, a <u>boll</u> grows in its place. The boll is the seed pod, which looks kind of like a walnut. When the boll dries, it splits open. Inside is the fluffy, white cotton. Farmers take the cotton to a <u>gin</u>. Machines at the gin take the cotton out of the bolls. The cotton is pressed into wrapped bundles called <u>bale</u>s. The bales are sent to cotton mills where the cotton is spun into <u>yarn</u>. The yarn is woven into <u>fabric</u>, or cloth. Then it is made into clothes, sheets, curtains, towels, and many other things.

Draw a line from the word to its picture. The story will help you.

flowers •

boll •

gin •

• bales

• yarn

• fabric

Colour the things below that could be made from cotton. Put an X on things that are not made of cotton.

Draw and colour the clothes that you are wearing today. Put an X on the ones made of cotton.

Busy as a Bee

Bees are hardworking insects. They live together in a nest called a <u>hive.</u> There is one <u>queen bee</u> in each hive. She is the largest bee. There are hundreds of <u>worker bees</u>. The worker bees fly from flower to flower gathering a sweet liquid called <u>nectar</u>. They make honey from the nectar and store it in little rooms in the hive. Each little room is a <u>cell</u>. Many cells in a row make a <u>honeycomb</u>. When a bear or a person tries to steal the honey, the bees swarm, flying around in large groups. Each bee has a <u>stinger</u> to protect it from its enemies. A person who is a <u>beekeeper</u> makes wooden hives for bees, then sells the honey when the bees finish making it.

Look at the picture below. Use each underlined word in the story to label the pictures.

On a piece of paper, make a list of five other insects. You may need an encyclopedia to help you.

An Active Volcano

Mount St. Helens is an active volcano in the United States. In 1980, this volcano erupted, spewing hot lava into the air. Explosions caused a huge cloud of ash. This grey ash filled the air and settled on houses and cars many kilometres away. The thick dust made it hard for people and animals to breathe. The explosions flattened trees on the side of the mountain. The hot rocks caused forest fires. The snow that was on the mountain melted quickly, causing floods and mud slides. Mount St. Helens still erupts from time to time but not as badly as it did in 1980.

Read each phrase below. Write the number of each phrase in the explosion of the volcano that correctly completes the sentence.

1. **Mount St. Helens erupted,**

2. **The thick ash made it hard**

3. **The explosions**

4. **The hot rocks caused**

5. **Melting snow caused**

6. **Because Mount St. Helens is an active volcano,**

forest fires.

flattened trees.

it still erupts from time to time.

for people and animals to breathe.

spewing hot lava and ash into the air.

floods and mudslides.

Write a story that begins this way:
We were camping in the mountains, when all of a sudden a volcano erupted!

A Play

 A **play** is a story written as a script. Actors read the script, then memorize their lines, so they can pretend to be the characters in the story. Read the play below. The words in parentheses tell the actors what to do.

A Bad Idea

(Megan and Kyle are talking before class starts.)

Megan: Hey, Kyle, are you ready for the big test today? I studied that list of words and the definitions for two hours last night.

Kyle: Oh, brother! I didn't study at all. I just wrote all the answers on the palm of my hand, see?

Megan: Kyle! You can't do that! That's cheating!

Kyle: Hey, don't worry. I won't get caught. Mrs. King will never know. *(Teacher passes out the tests.)*

Mrs. King: Okay, no more talking. Everyone keep your eyes on your own paper, and cover your answers with a cover sheet. You may begin. *(Kyle looks at his hand when the teacher isn't looking.)*

Joe: *(raising his hand)* Mrs. King, may I get a drink? I have the hiccups.

Mrs. King: Yes, you may.

Kyle: *(raising his hand)* Mrs. King, may I get a drink, too?

Mrs. King: Kyle, what is that on your hand? I think you better come to my desk.

Kyle: *(looks over at Megan)* Oh no . . .

Megan: Busted!

Use markers or crayons to follow each direction.

1. The words in parentheses are called *stage directions.* Underline all the stage directions with a blue line.

2. Highlight Megan's words in pink.

3. Highlight Kyle's words in yellow.

4. Highlight Mrs. King's words in green.

5. Highlight Joe's words in orange.

The writing assignment in Ms. Daniels' class was to write about someone you admire. Read what one student wrote.

Lunch Lady

by Karen Jackson

I don't know her name. She is one of the workers in our school cafeteria. I just call her Lunch Lady. She's my friend. There are several nice ladies in the cafeteria, but the Lunch Lady is the nicest of all. Every day she smiles at me when I go through the line. She says things like, "Hi Karen! Are you having a good day?" Lunch Lady always remembers that I like chicken nuggets the best. Whenever that is what is being served, she hands me the chicken nuggets and says, "Look, your favourite!" One day, I tripped and dropped my tray. Food went all over the floor. I was so embarrassed, but Lunch Lady came to my rescue. She helped me pick up the mess, and she told me, "Don't worry about it. It's okay." That made me feel better. Another time, I was at the shoe store with my mom, and I saw Lunch Lady. She gave me a big hug. The reason I admire Lunch Lady is because she is friendly and kind.

Read each sentence. Find the words that are wrong and cross them out. Then above them write the correct word or words that make the sentence true.

1. Karen wrote about Lunch Man.

2. Karen's favourite food is hot dogs.

3. Lunch Lady frowns when Karen comes through the line.

4. When Karen dropped her tray, Miss Daniels helped her.

5. One time, Karen saw the Lunch Lady at the hardware store.

6. Karen admires Lunch Lady because she is friendly and mean.

 Write a paragraph about someone you admire.

Chain Reaction

 *In a story, there is usually a reason something happens. This is the **cause**. What happened as a result is the **effect**.*

It was a long way to Aunt Ruth's house. Terry and Mary Beth started getting a little bit too loud in the back seat, so Dad said, "Girls, settle down. Be quiet and read your books." They knew Dad meant business. Just then, Mary Beth saw a bee flying around in the car. Her eyes got big, and she ducked her head, swatting the bee away. Terry looked at her, and Mary Beth loudly whispered, "BEEEE!" Terry wanted to scream, but she knew Dad would get mad. "What are you two doing back there?" Dad asked. Just then, the bee landed on Dad's bald head. Mary Beth knew she had to save him from getting stung, so she whopped Dad on the head with her book. Dad jerked the steering wheel, and the car ran off the road and through a fence. The cows that were in the field ran away. Later, a police officer gave Dad a ticket for reckless driving.

Draw a line to match the cause to the effect.

The girls got too loud, so	which let the cows out.
The girls saw a bee land on Dad's bald head, so	Dad said to be quiet.
The car ran off the road and through a fence	Mary Beth whopped Dad on the head with a book.

Keep the chain going! Write what happened next because Dad got a ticket.

Name _____

My Favourite Dentist

 A **character** *is a person or animal in a story. To understand a character better, you should pay attention to the details a story often gives about the character.*

Some kids are scared to go to the dentist, but not me. I have a funny dentist. His name is Dr. Smileyface. I don't think that's his real name, but that's what he tells all the kids who come to see him. He has a cool waiting room. It has video games and a big toy box. Dr. Smileyface always wears funny hats. Sometimes he has his face painted. He asks funny questions like "Are you married yet?" and "Do you eat flowers to make your breath smell so sweet?" That makes me laugh. One time, he told me this joke, "What has lots of teeth but never goes to the dentist? A comb!" When I laughed, he pulled my tooth. It didn't hurt at all! He also teaches me how to take care of my teeth because he says he doesn't want me to get a cavity the size of the Grand Canyon. Before I go home, he always gives me a surprise. Last time I went, he gave me a rubber spider to scare my mom with!

Colour the pictures that could be Dr. Smileyface. Put an X on the pictures that could not not be him.

Draw a line from the toothbrush to the box that makes the sentence true.

6. Dr. Smileyface makes
7. The child who wrote this story
8. Dr. Smileyface teaches kids
9. Dr. Smileyface sends kids home

how to take care of their teeth.

with a surprise.

his patients laugh.

is not afraid to go to the dentist.

What a Kid!

Tad is a very thoughtful boy. He is a person who uses a wheelchair. He was born with a disease that made him unable to walk. Tad likes reading. He also enjoys making other people happy. He called the Green Oaks School for the Blind and asked if he could volunteer. They said, "Sure!" Tad went to the school and quickly made friends. Every day, he reads books to the younger children. He plays games with them. Sometimes he helps them with their math. The children at the school nicknamed him Lucky because they feel so lucky to have him as a friend. That makes Tad very happy!

- If Tad uses a wheelchair, write an H in Box 1 and Box 10. If not, write a J in both boxes.

- If Tad doesn't like reading, write a U in Box 2 and Box 11. If he does, write a E in both boxes.

- If Tad looks for ways to make people happy, write an L in Box 3. If he doesn't, write a B.

- If Tad volunteers at the River Oak School, write a Z in Box 4. If that is not correct, write a P.

- If Tad reads to the younger children, write an N in Box 6. If not, write a V.

- If Tad plays games with the children, write a G in Box 7. If not, write a D.

- If Tad helps them with their math, write an O in Box 8. If not, write an R.

- If the children nicknamed Tad "Grumpy," write a K in Box 9. If not, write a T.

- If Tad is a happy person, write an R in Box 12. If not, write a C.

This part of the story is so funny!

Tad's secret of happiness is

					I	
1	2	3	4	5	6	7

					S
8	9	10	11	12	13

Limericks

 A **limerick** is a poem that has five lines in it. It is usually funny and has a special order of rhyming words. The first two lines rhyme. Then the next two lines rhyme. Then the last line rhymes with the first two lines. Read the limerick below.

There once was a fellow named Jed

Who spent too much time in his bed.

He slept for so long

That something went wrong,

His hair grew long on his head.

In the limerick above, draw a red circle around the three words that rhyme. Draw a green box around the two words that rhyme.

Help finish the limerick below by filling in the blanks with a word from the Word Bank.

Word Bank

class   lazy   pass   crazy   Daisy

There once was a student named ___ ___ ___ ___ ___

Who wouldn't work because she was ___ ___ ___ ___

She slept during ___ ___ ___ ___ ___.

No way she could ___ ___ ___ ___.

Her poor teacher finally went ___ ___ ___ ___ ___.

Work with a partner and write a limerick. It helps to start with three rhyming words and two other rhyming words, then make up the sentences.

A Tall Tale

 A **tall tale** is a story about a superhuman hero. The story is funny because everything is exaggerated. That means it is much bigger and better than real life. Read the tall tale below. Use a yellow crayon or marker to highlight each thing that is exaggerated.

Paul Bunyan

Paul Bunyan was a mighty man. He was so big, he had to use wagon wheels for buttons. Paul was a lumberjack. He owned a blue ox named Babe. Paul and Babe were so big that their tracks made 10,000 lakes in Minnesota in the United States.

Paul worked with seven axemen. They were so big that they were six feet tall sitting down. All of them were named Elmer. So when Paul called "Elmer!" they all came running.

The year of the two winters, it got so cold that when the axemen would speak, their words froze in midair. When it thawed in the spring, there was a terrible chatter for weeks.

One time Paul caught two giant mosquitoes and used them to drill holes in maple trees.

Paul Bunyan had a purple cow named Lucy. In the year of two winters, it got so cold that Lucy's milk turned to ice cream before it hit the pail.

The End

 Choose two funny sentences above and copy them on another piece of paper. Then draw a picture about each one.

My Favourite Books

Write a list of some books or stories you like. Which one is your favourite?
Draw a picture of the best part of your favourite story to make a cover.

_____

_____

_____

_____

_____

TESTS: READING

Name _____

Reading Skills Practise Test 1

Do the samples with a helper.

A. Phonic Analysis: Consonants

Look at each picture.
Write the missing letter or letters on the blank line.

Sample _____**at**	**1.** _____**indow**	**2.** _____**eese**
3. _____**ip**	**4.** _____**og**	**5.** _____**amp**
6. **ha**_____	**7.** **tee**_____	**8.** **tru**_____

B. Dictation

Listen to someone say words 1., 2., and 3. above. Write them here.

Sample _____   _____

_ _ _ _ _ _ _ _ _ _ _ _ _ _ _ _ _ _   **1.** _ _ _ _ _ _ _ _ _ _ _ _ _ _ _ _ _

_____   _____

2. _ _ _ _ _ _ _ _ _ _ _ _ _ _ _ _ _   **3.** _ _ _ _ _ _ _ _ _ _ _ _ _ _ _ _ _

_____   _____

C. Vocabulary: Picture-Word Match

Fill in the bubble next to the word that names each picture.

Sample	1.	2.
O girl O gift O giraffe	O life O leaf O leak	O ball O barn O bull
3. O main O mine O moon	**4.** O box O boy O boil	**5.** O mice O mound O mouse

D. High-Frequency Word Match

Fill in the bubble next to the word someone says aloud.

Sample	1.	2.
O the O this O thick	O of O over O or	O fun O from O fresh
3. O has O had O have	**4.** O when O where O which	**5.** O throw O through O thing

E. Grammar, Usage and Mechanics

Read each sentence. Fill in the bubble next to the word or words that best fit in the blank.

Sample	_____ ran up the hill.

- ○ he
- ○ He
- ○ He's

1. Did you take that book _____

- ○ home.
- ○ home
- ○ home?

2. We _____ outside all day.

- ○ plays
- ○ played
- ○ playing

3. _____ is our teacher this year.

- ○ mrs smith
- ○ Mrs Smith
- ○ Mrs. Smith

4. _____ is in my class.

- ○ Maria
- ○ maria
- ○ MARIA

5. I _____ have any homework last week.

- ○ didnt
- ○ didnt'
- ○ didn't

F. Story Comprehension
Read the story. Then answer each question.
Fill in the bubble next to the best answer.

Frogs lay their eggs in ponds. The eggs grow. Slowly, they turn into tadpoles. The tadpoles grow and change. They become frogs.

The frogs hop. They can hop onto land. They can even hop onto rocks in the pond. Frogs stay near the pond. There they can get water. They can also catch bugs to eat.

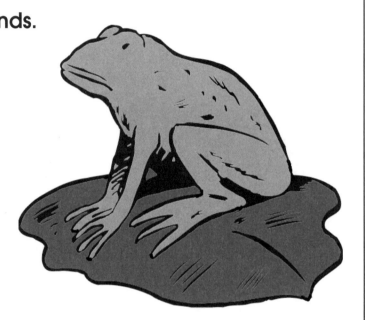

1. Where do frogs lay their eggs?
   O   on lily pads
   O   in ponds
   O   under rocks

2. What is a good title (name) for this story?
   O   Farm Animals
   O   Kittens Play
   O   Frogs

3. What does a tadpole become?
   O   a fish
   O   a frog
   O   an egg

4. What do frogs eat?
   O   rocks
   O   bugs
   O   hay

Reading Skills Practise Test 2

Do the samples with a helper.

A. Phonic Analysis: Consonants
Look at each picture.
Write the missing letter or letters on the blank line.

Sample	1.	2.
_____ar	_____ock	_____ain
3.	4.	5.
ne _____	_____at	fi_____

B. Phonic Analysis: Vowels
Look at each picture.
Write the missing letter or letters on the blank line.

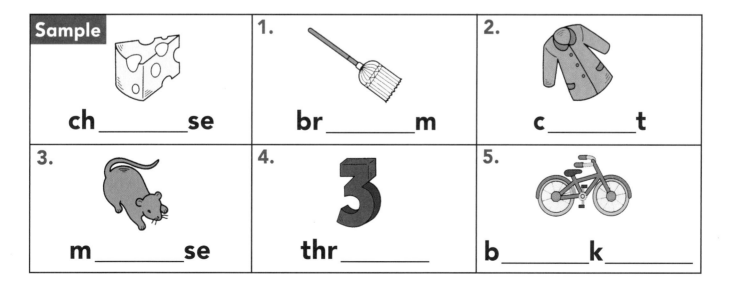

Sample	1.	2.
ch_____se	br_____m	c_____t
3.	4.	5.
m_____se	thr_____	b_____k_____

C. Dictation
Listen to someone say the words from B1., 2., and 3. Write them here.

Sample

_____   _____

-        -

_____   **1.** _____

_____   _____

-        -

2. _____   **3.** _____

D. High-Frequency Word Match
Fill in the bubble next to the word someone says aloud.

Sample	**1.**	**2.**
O when O where O which	O over O of O off	O every O vest O very
3.	**4.**	**5.**
O knew O know O knot	O cook O coat O could	O some O something O summer

E. Grammar, Usage and Mechanics

Read each sentence. Fill in the bubble next to the word or words that best fit in the blank.

Sample _____ plays in the park.
- ○ he
- ○ He
- ○ He's

1. Did you see that _____
- ○ star.
- ○ star
- ○ star?

2. We _____ in the yard.
- ○ runs
- ○ run
- ○ running

3. _____ is my neighbour.
- ○ mr smith
- ○ Mr Smith
- ○ Mr. Smith

4. She moved to _____
- ○ Toronto.
- ○ toronto.
- ○ TORONTO.

5. He _____ come to my house today.
- ○ cant
- ○ cant'
- ○ can't

6. Watch _____
- ○ out.
- ○ out!
- ○ out?

7. The dog _____ the cat.
- ○ chased
- ○ chasing
- ○ chase

8. _____ is nice.
- ○ dr hamilton
- ○ Dr Hamilton
- ○ Dr. Hamilton

9. We went to _____
- ○ alberta.
- ○ ALBERTA.
- ○ Alberta.

F. Story Comprehension

Read the story. Then answer each question.
Fill in the bubble next to the best answer.

A whale is a very big animal. Whales live in the sea. Some whales swim with each other. They travel in large groups, called pods. They swim around, looking for food.

Whales feed on sea life. Some whales eat tiny plants and animals called plankton. Other whales have teeth and can eat seals and small fish.

Whales must stay wet all the time. However, they also must come to the top of the sea to breathe. When a whale leaps out of the water to catch a breath of air, it is an amazing sight.

1. What are pods?
- O whale food
- O groups of whales
- O sea animals

2. What is a good title (name) for this story?
- O The Sea
- O Fish
- O Whales

3. What must all whales do?
- O eat seals and fish
- O spend time on land
- O stay wet

4. Why do whales sometimes jump out of the water?
- O to warm up
- O to get air
- O to catch fish

Name _____

Reading Skills Practise Test 3

Do the samples with a helper.

A. Phonic Analysis: Consonants
Look at each picture.
Write the missing letter or letters on the blank line.

Sample	**1.**	**2.**
_____ar	_____ed	_____ock
3.	**4.**	**5.**
_____apes	ha_____	too_____

B. Phonic Analysis: Vowels
Look at each picture.
Write the missing letter or letters on the line.

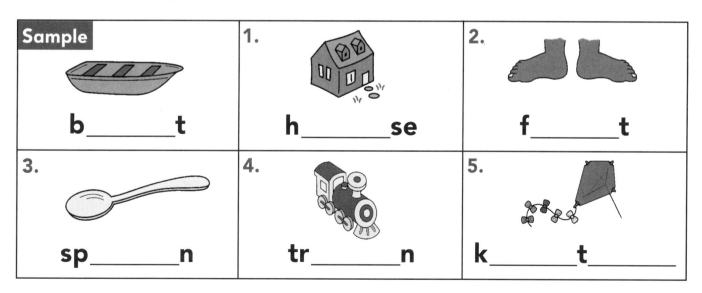

Sample	**1.**	**2.**
b_____t	h_____se	f_____t
3.	**4.**	**5.**
sp_____n	tr_____n	k_____t_____

C. Dictation

Listen to someone say the words from B 1., 2., and 3. Write them here.

Sample

_____

- - - - - - - - - - - - - - -

_____

_____   1. _____

- - - - - - - - - - - - - - -

_____   _____

- - - - - - - - - - - - - - -

2. _____   3. _____

D. High-Frequency Word Match

Fill in the bubble next to the word someone says aloud.

Sample	**1.**	**2.**
◯ where ◯ then ◯ there	◯ above ◯ about ◯ away	◯ shall ◯ ship ◯ should
3.	**4.**	**5.**
◯ those ◯ this ◯ though	◯ know ◯ knew ◯ now	◯ every ◯ something ◯ everything

E. Grammar, Usage and Mechanics

Read each sentence. Fill in the bubble next to the word or words that best fit in the blank.

Sample _____ walk to school.
- ◯ they
- ◯ she
- ◯ They

1. I _____ my bike in the park.
- ◯ rides
- ◯ ride
- ◯ riding

2. Can you lift this _____
- ◯ box?
- ◯ box
- ◯ box.

3. My friend's name is _____
- ◯ peter Jones.
- ◯ Peter Jones.
- ◯ Peter Jones

4. We live in _____
- ◯ manitoba.
- ◯ Manitoba.
- ◯ MANITOBA.

5. Be _____
- ◯ careful!
- ◯ careful.
- ◯ careful?

6. I _____ want to play.
- ◯ dont'
- ◯ dont
- ◯ don't

7. We _____ at his house.
- ◯ playing
- ◯ played
- ◯ plays

8. _____ on her way home.
- ◯ she's
- ◯ She
- ◯ She's

9. Our family doctor is _____.
- ◯ dr. Levchuck
- ◯ Dr. Levchuck
- ◯ Dr Levchuck

Name _____

F. Story Comprehension

Read the story. Then answer each question.
Fill in the bubble next to the best answer.

A tornado is a kind of wind storm. The winds can be very strong. A tornado is shaped like a funnel. Sometimes, a tornado is called a "twister."

Most tornadoes take place in June, July, or August. They usually happen on hot days.

A tornado does not last long. But it can wreck everything in its path! When a tornado comes, the safest place to be is below ground. That's why people often go to their basements before a tornado comes.

1. What is a good title (name) for this story?

  O Storms
  O Tornadoes
  O Wind

2. What is a twister?

  O a basement
  O a tornado
  O a hard rain

3. When do tornadoes usually happen?

  O only in June
  O in winter
  O on hot days

4. Why do people go to their basements before a tornado comes?

  O to be safe
  O to watch the storm
  O to play games

Reading Skills Practise Test 4

Do the samples with a helper.

A. Phonic Analysis: Consonants
Look at each picture.
Write the missing letter or letters on the blank line.

Sample	1.	2.
_____**oom**	_____**ag**	_____**oon**
3.	4.	5.
_____**ake**	**ri**_____	**tru**_____

B. Phonic Analysis: Vowels
Look at each picture.
Write the missing letter or letters on the line.

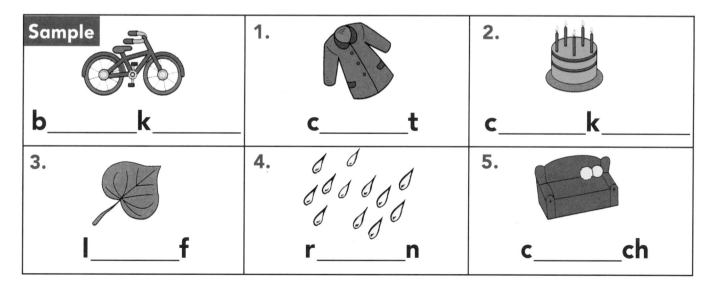

Sample	1.	2.
b_____**k**_____	**c**_____**t**	**c**_____**k**_____
3.	4.	5.
l_____**f**	**r**_____**n**	**c**_____**ch**

C. Phonemic Awareness

Write the number of syllables in these words after someone says them aloud.

(sample) pencil   1. tomato   2. map   3. information   4. bookmark   5. elephant

Sample _____   **1.** _____   **2.** _____

3. _____   **4.** _____   **5.** _____

D. High-Frequency Word Match

Fill in the bubble next to the word someone says aloud.

Sample	1.	2.
○ when ○ how ○ who	○ after ○ afraid ○ often	○ skate ○ school ○ shore
3.	**4.**	**5.**
○ between ○ because ○ beneath	○ might ○ mice ○ mitten	○ knew ○ now ○ know

Name _____

E. Grammar, Usage and Mechanics

Read each sentence. Fill in the bubble next to
the word or words that best complete each sentence.

Sample _____ walk to school.

- ◯ She
- ◯ We
- ◯ they

1. The boys _____ their
pictures.

- ◯ colours
- ◯ colouring
- ◯ colour

2. Yesterday, I _____ with
my friend.

- ◯ played
- ◯ play
- ◯ plays

3. What is in your _____

- ◯ bag?
- ◯ bag.
- ◯ bag

4. Look _____

- ◯ out
- ◯ out!
- ◯ out?

5. My dog _____ run.

- ◯ won't
- ◯ wont
- ◯ wont'

6. _____ going to the fair.

- ◯ She
- ◯ shes'
- ◯ She's

7. My mother _____ me a
new coat next week.

- ◯ will buy
- ◯ buy
- ◯ bought

8. I went on a trip to ____

- ◯ nunavut.
- ◯ NUNAVUT
- ◯ Nunavut.

9. _____ gave me a
checkup.

- ◯ dr. Singh
- ◯ Dr. Singh
- ◯ Dr Singh

Name _____

F. Story Comprehension

Read the story. Then answer each question.
Fill in the bubble next to the best answer.

> Tigers are the world's biggest cats. Most tigers are bigger than lions. A tiger's body can be as long as a car. A tiger can even weigh as much as two adult people!
>
> Tigers are good hunters. Why? They are good at jumping. They are fast. They can see well in the dark. When tigers hunt at night, they surprise other animals. A tiger's favourite foods are deer and wild pigs. They also eat other animals, like monkeys, buffalo, and goats.
>
> Tigers live in Asia. They live in different types of homes. Some tigers live in rainforests. Others live in the woods, swamps, or grasslands.

1. What is a good title (name) for this story?

   ○ Animals

   ○ Cats

   ○ Tigers

2. What animals do tigers often eat?

   ○ deer and wild pigs

   ○ pigs and dogs

   ○ birds and lions

3. Where do tigers live?

   ○ Africa

   ○ Mexico

   ○ Asia

4. Write a sentence telling why tigers are good hunters.

_____

_____

_____

Reading Skills Practise Test 5

Do the samples with a helper.

A. Phonic Analysis: Consonants
Look at each picture.
Write the missing letter or letters on the blank line.

Sample	1.	2.
_____ee	_____air	_____ane
3.	4.	5.
_____ake	ne_____	fi_____

B. Phonic Analysis: Vowels
Look at each picture.
Write the missing letter or letters on the blank line.

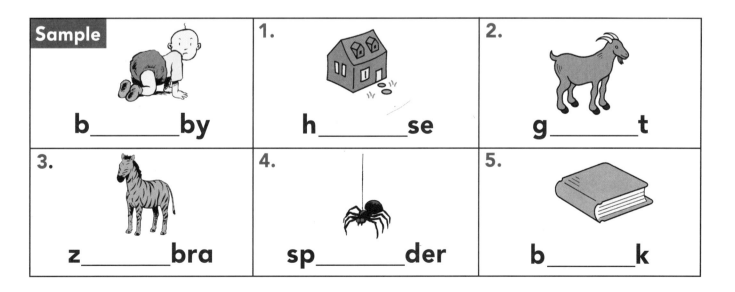

Sample	1.	2.
b_____by	h_____se	g_____t
3.	4.	5.
z_____bra	sp_____der	b_____k

C. Dictation

Listen to someone say the words from B 1., 2., and 3. Write them here.

Sample

_____

- - - - - - - - - - - - - - - - - -   - - - - - - - - - - - - - - - - - -

_____   1._____

_____   _____

- - - - - - - - - - - - - - - - - -   - - - - - - - - - - - - - - - - - -

2._____   3._____

D. High-Frequency Word Match

Fill in the bubble next to the word someone says aloud.

Sample	1.	2.
○ when ○ why ○ which	○ over ○ or ○ off	○ every ○ vest ○ very
3.	4.	5.
○ knew ○ know ○ knot	○ will ○ weed ○ would	○ tugging ○ together ○ teacher

E. Grammar, Usage and Mechanics

Read each sentence. Fill in the bubble next to the word or words that best fit in the blank.

Sample _____ ran in the park.
- ○ she
- ○ She
- ○ She's

1. Did you read that _____
- ○ book.
- ○ Book.
- ○ book?

2. We _____ in the lake.
- ○ swims
- ○ swam
- ○ swimming

3. _____ is my dentist.
- ○ dr bell
- ○ Dr Bell
- ○ Dr. Bell

4. She lives in _____
- ○ Centreville.
- ○ centreville.
- ○ CENTREVILLE.

5. He _____ be at the soccer game.
- ○ wont
- ○ wont'
- ○ won't

6. Watch _____
- ○ out.
- ○ out!
- ○ out?

7. The rabbit _____ to the carrot.
- ○ hoped
- ○ hopping
- ○ hopped

8. _____ drove the school bus.
- ○ mrs campbell
- ○ Mrs Campbell
- ○ Mrs. Campbell

9. We took a trip to _____
- ○ halifax.
- ○ HALIFAX.
- ○ Halifax.

10. I _____ go to the park.
- ○ couldnt
- ○ couldn't
- ○ couldnt'

F. Story Comprehension
Read the story. Then answer each question.
Fill in the bubble next to the best answer.

   Many animals have claws. Claws are like your fingernails. Animal claws can be long or short. Most claws are very sharp.

   Claws have many uses. Birds have claws called talons. These claws help them to hold on to things and to catch their food. Bears have claws on their large paws. They use their claws to get food and to climb up trees. Cats have claws that help them to climb and hold on to things. Cats like to scratch with their claws. Scratching keeps their claws sharp.

1. What are talons?
- O cat claws
- O bird claws
- O bear claws

2. What is a good title (name) for this story?
- O Birds
- O Climbing
- O Claws

3. How do animals use claws?
- O to hold on to things
- O to write in the sand
- O to swim in the ocean

4. Which animal has claws?
- O fish
- O bear
- O snake

Reading Skills Practise Test 6

Do the samples with a helper.

A. Phonic Analysis: Consonants
Look at each picture.
Write the missing letter or letters on the blank line.

Sample	1.	2.
_____ar	_____apes	_____ide
3.	**4.**	**5.**
_____anch	ha_____	clo_____

B. Phonic Analysis: Vowels
Look at each picture.
Write the missing letter or letters on the line.

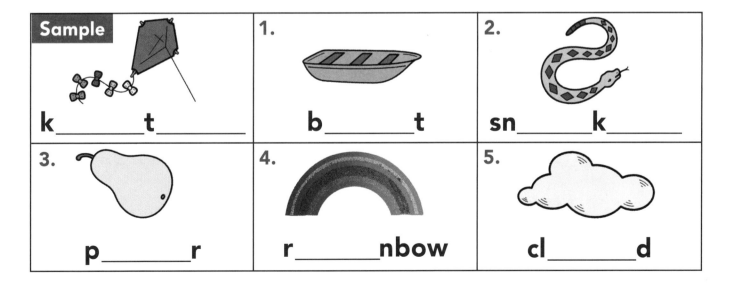

Sample	1.	2.
k____t_____	b_____t	sn____k____
3.	**4.**	**5.**
p_____r	r_____nbow	cl_____d

C. Phonemic Awareness

Write the number of syllables in these words after someone says them out loud: (sample) apple 1. soup 2. cartwheel 3. television 4. shirt 5. animals

Sample _____   **1.** _____   **2.** _____

3. _____   **4.** _____   **5.** _____

D. Grammar, Usage and Mechanics

Read each sentence. Fill in the bubble next to the word or words that best complete each sentence.

Sample _____ rides a horse.
- ◯ she
- ◯ She
- ◯ We

1. The children _____ soccer.
- ◯ play
- ◯ plays
- ◯ playing

2. Last night, we _____ a great movie.
- ◯ watch
- ◯ watching
- ◯ watched

3. Which story is _____
- ◯ yours!
- ◯ yours.
- ◯ yours?

4. That frog _____ jump.
- ◯ wont
- ◯ wont'
- ◯ won't

5. _____ going to the zoo.
- ◯ He's
- ◯ He
- ◯ Hes'

6. My book _____ in the mail tomorrow.
- ◯ came
- ◯ come
- ◯ will come

7. _____ read a story to us.
- ◯ ms. Cohen
- ◯ Ms Cohen
- ◯ Ms. Cohen

E. Story Comprehension

Read the story. Then answer each question.
Fill in the bubble next to the best answer.

A baby elephant grows up with its family, or *herd*. A herd is made up of mothers, sisters, cousins, and aunts.

The herd takes care of the *calf*, or baby elephant, in many ways. A mother stands over her calf to keep it safe from danger and the hot sun. An aunt helps the calf keep up when the herd is walking. When an enemy is near, the adult elephants stand in front of the calf. Then, the oldest female fans out her ears to look big and angry. The herd doesn't want anything to happen to the calf.

1. What is a good title (name) for this story?

○ Mother Elephants
○ Elephant Herds
○ Adult Elephants

2. What is a calf?

○ a baby elephant
○ the oldest elephant
○ an elephant family

3. When an elephant fans out its ears, it looks _____.

○ big and funny
○ small and angry
○ big and angry

4. Write a sentence telling one way the herd helps the baby.

_____

_____

_____

F. Story Comprehension

Read the story. Then answer each question.
Fill in the bubble next to the best answer.

> Chinese New Year is the most important Chinese holiday. It celebrates the end of one year and the beginning of a new year. The holiday falls in January or February and lasts for 15 days.
>
> People do many things to get ready for Chinese New Year. They clean and decorate their homes. They buy flowers and new clothes.
>
>
>
> When the holiday starts, people visit with family and friends. They gather for a big feast. They also go to parades, where they see dancers, drummers, and colourful dragons.

1. What is a good title (name) for this story?

- O Dragons
- O China
- O Chinese New Year

2. Chinese New Year lasts for how long?

- O 24 days
- O 15 days
- O one year

3. People get ready for the holiday by _____.

- O cleaning their homes
- O dancing
- O going to parades

4. Write a sentence telling some ways that people celebrate Chinese New Year. _____

_____

_____

Reading Skills Practise Test 7

Do the samples with a helper.

A. Phonic Analysis: Consonants
Look at each picture.
Write the missing letter or letters on the blank line.

Sample	1.	2.
_____ider	wat_____	_____an
3.	**4.**	**5.**
_____ant	lo_____	bo_____

B. Phonic Analysis: Vowels
Look at each picture.
Write the missing letter or letters on the line.

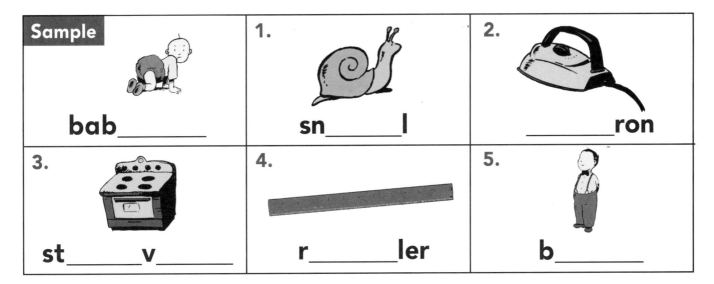

Sample	1.	2.
bab_____	sn_____l	_____ron
3.	**4.**	**5.**
st_____v_____	r_____ler	b_____

Name _____

C. Phonemic Awareness

Write the number of syllables in these words after someone says them aloud: (sample) paper 1. elephant 2. ice 3. information 4. principal 5. apple

| Sample | 1. | 2. |

Sample _____ **1.** _____ **2.** _____

3. _____ **4.** _____ **5.** _____

D. Grammar, Usage and Mechanics

Read each sentence. Fill in the bubble next to the word or words that best complete each sentence.

Sample _____ live in a city.
- O they
- O They
- O He

1. The farm animals _____ grain.
- O eating
- O eats
- O eat

2. Today, we will _____ the dog a bath.
- O gived
- O giving
- O give

3. Ouch! A bee stung _____
- O Me.
- O me?
- O me!

4. I _____ swim in the deep water yet.
- O cant
- O can't
- O cant'

5. _____ going to the library.
- O She's
- O Shes
- O Shes'

6. My aunt _____ me to the movies tomorrow.
- O take
- O took
- O will take

7. _____ fixed my bike.
- O Mr. O'Connor
- O mr. O'Connor
- O Mr O'Connor

Name _____

E. Story Comprehension

Read the story. Then answer each question.
Fill in the bubble next to the best answer.

Kwanzaa is a holiday celebrated by some people who have African ancestors. The word ancestors means family who lived before you — like your great, great, great grandparents. Kwanzaa celebrates families and sticking together. It always lasts for seven days, beginning on December 26th and ending on January 1st.

People do many things to celebrate Kwanzaa. They dress in special clothes and decorate their homes with fruits and vegetables. Families and friends get together for big meals. Children get gifts, like books and toys.

One of the most important parts of Kwanzaa is lighting candles in the kinara. The kinara is a special candle holder with seven candles. People who celebrate Kwanzaa light one candle each night.

1. What is a good title (name) for this story?
○ Kwanzaa
○ Children Get Gifts
○ Ancestors

2. Kwanzaa lasts for how many days?
○ 1
○ 7
○ 26

3. A kinara is a
○ kind of clothing
○ kind of food
○ kind of candle holder

4. Write a sentence telling some ways that people celebrate Kwanzaa.

_____

_____

Name _____

F. Reading a Graph

Look at the graph. Then answer each question. Fill in the bubble next to the best answer.

Lost Teeth
Hardy School, Grade 2

Number of Teeth Lost

Teeth							
7	😀	😀					
6	😀	😀	😀	😀			
5							
4	😀	😀	😀	😀	😀	😀	
3	😀	😀	😀	😀			
2	😀	😀	😀				
1	😀						

😀 equals one student.

1. What is this graph about?
  ○ which students like teeth
  ○ Hardy School
  ○ how many teeth students have lost

2. How many students have lost six teeth?
  ○ 2 students
  ○ 3 students
  ○ 4 students

3. What's the largest number of teeth that any student has lost?
  ○ 4
  ○ 7
  ○ 20

4. How many students have lost five teeth?
  ○ 0
  ○ 1
  ○ 2

Name _____

Reading Skills Practise Test 8

Do the samples with a helper.

A. Phonic Analysis: Consonants
Look at each picture.
Write the missing letter or letters on the blank line.

Sample	1.	2.
_____ar	_____ale	_____ower
3.	**4.**	**5.**
_____ree	de_____	_____ebra

B. Phonic Analysis: Vowels
Look at each picture.
Write the missing letters on the blank line.

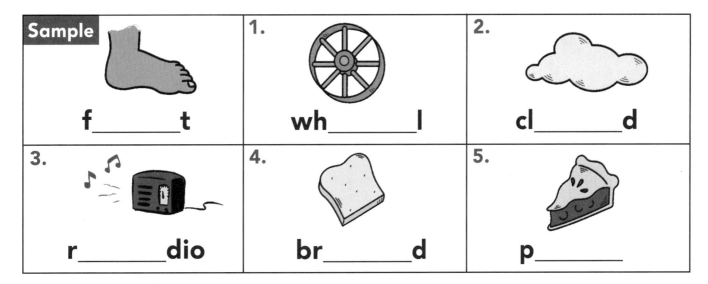

Sample	1.	2.
f_____t	wh_____l	cl_____d
3.	**4.**	**5.**
r_____dio	br_____d	p_____

Name _____

C. Grammar, Usage and Mechanics

Read each sentence. Fill in the bubble next to the word or words that best fit in the blank.

Sample _____ go to the park.
- O we
- O We
- O We've

1. Can she run in the _____
- O race.
- O race
- O race?

2. They _____ baseball.
- O play
- O plays
- O playing

3. _____ is my teacher.
- O mrs miller
- O Mrs Miller
- O Mrs. Miller

4. She went on a trip to
_____.
- O calgary
- O Calgary
- O CALGARY

5. He _____ drive the car.
- O couldnt
- O couldnt'
- O couldn't

6. _____ There is a fire!
- O Help.
- O Help!
- O Help?

7. My aunt lives in _____.
- O Montreal, Quebec
- O montreal, quebec
- O Montreal Quebec

8. _____ eat out," said
Mom.
- O let's
- O Let's
- O "Let's

9. The children can _____
around the track.
- O ran
- O runs
- O run

D. Story Comprehension

Read the story. Then answer each question.
Fill in the bubble next to the best answer.

We get many useful things from trees. Wood comes from trees. The wood can be used to make houses, desks, and chairs. Rubber comes from trees. Rubber is used to make balls and boots. We also get fruit and nuts from trees. Birds and other animals like these tree treats, too.

Trees can be helpful. Some medicines are made from tree bark. These medicines help sick people get well. Trees also give us shade on a sunny day. Many animals make their homes in trees. Birds build nests on tree branches. Owls, foxes, and other animals can live in tree holes.

1. What is a good title (name) for this story?

○ Growing Trees
○ Animals and Trees
○ Trees Are Important

2. What do people <u>and</u> animals use from trees?

○ desks
○ food
○ rubber

3. What animal can make its home in a tree?

○ the fox
○ the horse
○ the elephant

4. What other thing might you make from a tree?

○ a car
○ a baseball bat
○ a computer

E. Reading a Graph

Look at the graph. Then answer each question.
Fill in the bubble next to the best answer.

Favourite Sports Mrs. Park's Class, Grade 2					
10			▓		
9			▓		
8			▓	▓	
7			▓	▓	
6			▓	▓	
5	▓		▓	▓	▓
4	▓		▓	▓	▓
3	▓		▓	▓	▓
2	▓	▓	▓	▓	▓
1	▓	▓	▓	▓	▓
number of students	baseball	football	soccer	gymnastics	skating

1. What is this graph about?
   ○ soccer and basketball
   ○ what sports kids like best
   ○ Mrs. Green's class

2. Which sport is liked by the most students?
   ○ soccer
   ○ skating
   ○ gymnastics

3. How many students like baseball best?
   ○ 2
   ○ 5
   ○ 7

4. Which 2 sports are liked by the same number of students?
   ○ baseball and soccer
   ○ gymnastics and soccer
   ○ skating and baseball

Reading Skills Practise Test 9

Do the samples with a helper.

A. Phonic Analysis: Consonants
Look at each picture.
Write the missing letter or letters on the blank line.

Sample	1.	2.
_____arn	_____eese	fi_____
3.	**4.**	**5.**
te_____	_____ush	_____own

B. Phonic Analysis: Vowels
Look at each picture.
Write the missing letter or letters on the line.

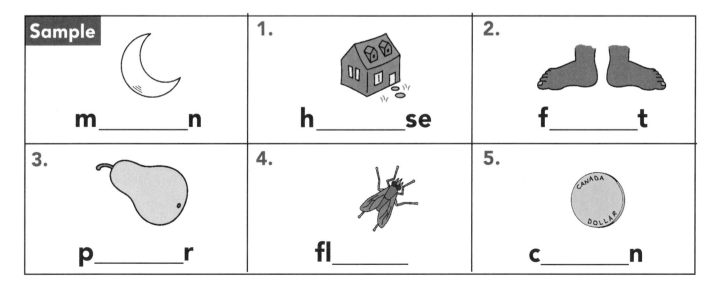

Sample	1.	2.
m_____n	h_____se	f_____t
3.	**4.**	**5.**
p_____r	fl_____	c_____n

C. Grammar, Usage and Mechanics

Read each sentence. Fill in the bubble next to the word or words that best fit in the blank.

Sample

_____ race down the hill.
- ○ We
- ○ we
- ○ She

1. May I go to the _____
- ○ store.
- ○ store?
- ○ Store?

2. _____ plays football every day.
- ○ he
- ○ He
- ○ They

3. I saw _____ at the park.
- ○ Mrs Walker
- ○ mrs. walker
- ○ Mrs. Walker

4. I will visit my uncle in _____
- ○ March.
- ○ march.
- ○ MARCH.

5. _____ You hit the ball hard.
- ○ Wow
- ○ Wow!
- ○ Wow.

6. I _____ run as fast as Sami.
- ○ cant
- ○ cant'
- ○ can't

7. _____ on my way," said Jane.
- ○ I'm
- ○ "Im
- ○ "I'm

8. Yesterday, we _____ our bikes.
- ○ ride
- ○ rode
- ○ riding

9. We will soon move to _____
- ○ Ontario.
- ○ Ontario
- ○ ontario.

D. Story Comprehension

Read the story. Then answer each question.
Fill in the bubble next to the best answer.

> Most people go to sleep at night. So do many animals. But a few animals sleep most of the day. Then they stay up all night. These animals can use their senses to get around in the dark.
>
> Owls, skunks, and moths all stay up at night. The owl has very large eyes that can see in the dark. Both the skunk and the moth have a very strong sense of smell. They can smell other animals from very far away.
>
> Why do some animals stay up all night? Sometimes, it's because nighttime is the best time to hunt. In hot places, animals can stay cooler at night. There are many reasons animals come out at night.

1. What is a good title (name) for this story?
   - O Owls
   - O Night Animals
   - O Sleep

2. What do both skunks and moths have?
   - O large eyes
   - O a strong sense of smell
   - O a bad smell

3. The owl's large eyes help it to
   - O see in the dark.
   - O see in the daytime.
   - O sleep very well.

4. What might be another reason to stay up at night?
   - O to get a suntan
   - O to grow food
   - O to hide from other animals

E. Reading a Graph

Look at the graph. Then answer each question.
Fill in the bubble next to the best answer.

STUDENTS' FAVOURITE COLOURS
Kensington School, Grade 2

COLOURS	1	2	3	4	5	6	7	8	9	10
red	■	■	■	■	■	■				
blue	■	■	■	■	■	■	■	■	■	
yellow	■	■	■	■						
green	■	■	■	■	■	■				

NUMBER OF STUDENTS

1. What is this graph about?
   ○ how colours are made
   ○ what colours students like best
   ○ Grade 2

2. How many students like red the best?
   ○ 7
   ○ 4
   ○ 6

3. Which two colours are liked by the same number of students?
   ○ red and blue
   ○ red and green
   ○ blue and green

4. How many more students like the colour blue better than the colour green?
   ○ 2
   ○ 3
   ○ 4

Reading Skills Practise Test 10

Do the samples with a helper.

A. Word-Match Dictation

Fill in the bubble next to the word that fits in the
sentence someone says out loud. (See sentences on page 407.)

Sample	1.	2.
○ two	○ deer	○ we're
○ too	○ dear	○ were
○ to	○ den	○ where
3.	**4.**	**5.**
○ knife	○ sent	○ there
○ night	○ scent	○ they're
○ knight	○ cent	○ their

B. Synonyms

Fill in the bubble next to the word that means the **same** as the **bold** word.

Sample	1.	2.
big ○ small ○ large ○ skinny	**happy** ○ sad ○ shy ○ glad	**fast** ○ funny ○ quick ○ slow
3.	**4.**	**5.**
answer ○ respond ○ ask ○ tell	**brave** ○ scared ○ proud ○ fearless	**mad** ○ furious ○ smart ○ laugh

C. Antonyms

Fill in the bubble next to the word that means the **opposite** of the
bold word.

Sample	1.	2.
day ○ school ○ time ○ night	**old** ○ young ○ age ○ long	**hot** ○ cold ○ warm ○ strange
3.	**4.**	**5.**
clean ○ nice ○ dirty ○ run	**tall** ○ high ○ smooth ○ short	**strong** ○ weak ○ powerful ○ wild

D. Grammar, Usage and Mechanics

Read each sentence. Fill in the bubble next to the word or words that best fit in the blank.

Sample

The boy walked _____
- ○ home
- ○ home.
- ○ home,

1. Where do you _____
- ○ live!
- ○ live
- ○ live?

2. Maria and I play _____
- ○ soccer.
- ○ soccer?
- ○ soccer

3. Our teacher is _____
- ○ mr. lee.
- ○ Mr. Lee.
- ○ mr. Lee.

4. We will _____ a movie tomorrow.
- ○ watch
- ○ watched
- ○ watches

5. Trish turned 8 years old on _____
- ○ February, 22. 2017
- ○ February 22, 2017.
- ○ February 22. 2017

6. _____ is in the north.
- ○ Yukon
- ○ yukon
- ○ YUKON

7. Yesterday, my mom _____ me with my homework.
- ○ helped
- ○ helps
- ○ helping

8. Owls _____ sleep at night.
- ○ don't
- ○ dont'
- ○ dono't

9. Jake is _____ than Ed.
- ○ more tall
- ○ taller
- ○ tallest

10. Is this _____ book?
- ○ them
- ○ us
- ○ your

11. We went for a ride in _____ car.
- ○ Mike's
- ○ mike's
- ○ Mike

E. Story and Graph Comprehension

Read the story and look at the graph. Then answer each question.
Fill in the bubble next to the best answer.

Watch out for tornadoes in summer! A tornado, or a twister, is a dangerous storm. Tornadoes form when air begins to spin under a thundercloud. The air whirls around very fast. It twists so fast that it can lift up a car or a tree.

Mr. Vert's Grade 2 class researched how many tornadoes hit Fay County in five years.

Look at the graph to see what they found out.

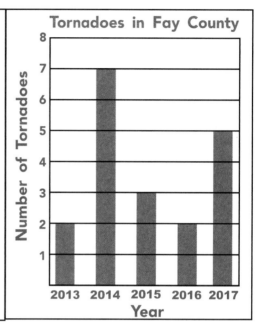

1. What is another name for a tornado?
   - ◯ cloud
   - ◯ hurricane
   - ◯ twister

2. When do you think most tornadoes take place?
   - ◯ summer
   - ◯ spring
   - ◯ winter

3. In which year did the most tornadoes hit Fay County?
   - ◯ 2013
   - ◯ 2014
   - ◯ 2015

4. How many more tornadoes were there in 2017 than in 2016?
   - ◯ 3
   - ◯ 4
   - ◯ 5

F. Story Comprehension

Read the story. Then answer each question.
Fill in the bubble next to the best answer.

> Spiders are carnivores. That means that they eat other animals to survive. Spiders eat insects.
>
> Different spiders have different ways to catch insects. A web weaver builds sticky webs to trap insects. A wandering hunter walks about in search of something to eat. When it sees an insect, it jumps on top of its prey. A tube dweller hides in the ground and waits for insects to come by. Then it springs up and catches its tasty meal.
>
> Spiders help people by eating insects. How? Spiders eat insects that destroy farmers' crops. Spiders also eat insects that carry diseases. So if you see a spider, let it be!

1. What is a good title (name) for this story?
   - ○ Wonderful Webs
   - ○ Insects Everywhere
   - ○ Hungry Spiders

2. A **carnivore** is an animal that eats other _____ .
   - ○ animals
   - ○ insects
   - ○ plants

3. How do spiders help people?
   - ○ They hide when people are near.
   - ○ They don't eat animals.
   - ○ They eat insects that destroy crops.

4. Write a sentence telling one or more ways a spider can catch its food.

   _____

   _____

Name _____

Reading Skills Practise Test 11

Do the samples with a helper.

A. Word-Match Dictation

Fill in the bubble next to the word that fits in the sentence someone says out loud. (See sentences on page 387.)

Sample	1.	2.
○ one	○ said	○ mad
○ won	○ sad	○ made
○ win	○ sand	○ mud
3.	**4.**	**5.**
○ pull	○ tore	○ hear
○ pill	○ tear	○ here
○ pail	○ tire	○ hair

B. Synonyms

Fill in the bubble next to the word that means the **same** as the **bold** word.

Sample	1.	2.
middle ○ centre	**child** ○ kid	**shut** ○ open
○ side	○ adult	○ lock
○ front	○ smiled	○ close
3.	**4.**	**5.**
look ○ hear	**says** ○ tells	**done** ○ completed
○ see	○ yells	○ behind
○ taste	○ plays	○ good

C. Antonyms

Fill in the bubble next to the word that means the **opposite** of the **bold** word.

Sample	1.	2.
many ○ few	**yours** ○ that	**long** ○ tall
○ a lot	○ mine	○ big
○ money	○ those	○ short
3.	**4.**	**5.**
quiet ○ loud	**grow** ○ rise	**more** ○ better
○ shy	○ shrink	○ big
○ silent	○ flower	○ less

D. Grammar, Usage and Mechanics

Read each sentence. Fill in the bubble next to the word or words that best fit in the blank.

Sample

It is time for _____
- ○ bed
- ○ bed.
- ○ bed,

1. Did you brush your _____
- ○ teeth?
- ○ teeth.
- ○ teeth

2. Pam and I played with _____
- ○ blocks
- ○ blocks.
- ○ Blocks.

3. School is over at _____
- ○ Three O'clock.
- ○ three o'clock
- ○ three o'clock.

4. Today I will ____ piano.
- ○ practise
- ○ practises
- ○ practising

5. What _____ you want for your birthday?
- ○ does
- ○ do
- ○ Do

6. _____ is where the Prime Minister lives.
- ○ Ottawa
- ○ ottawa
- ○ OTTAWA

7. Will you _____ me on the swing?
- ○ pushed
- ○ pushing
- ○ push

8. I am ____ reading this book.
- ○ finish
- ○ finished
- ○ Finish

9. ____ can ride a horse.
- ○ She
- ○ she
- ○ she's

10. Jack's brother will turn 5 on _____.
- ○ October 28, 2022
- ○ october 28, 2022
- ○ October 28. 2022

11. _____ cat has kittens.
- ○ Tim's
- ○ Tims
- ○ tim's

E. Story Comprehension
Read the story. Then answer each question.
Fill in the bubble next to the best answer.

> When you were born, you had 300 bones in your body! Why so many? They do many different jobs. Bones in your back, arms, and legs allow you to stand up and move around. Other bones protect your insides. Your skull, for example, is like a hard helmet for your brain. Your ribs protect your heart and lungs.
>
> Did you know that bones are alive? They are made of hard stuff and tiny living cells, so small you need a microscope to see them. The living cells help your bones grow as you get older. If you break a bone, the living cells help heal it.

1. When you were born, you had _____ bones.
   - ○ 100
   - ○ 200
   - ○ 300

2. Your skull protects your _____.
   - ○ brain
   - ○ arms
   - ○ legs

3. What is in your bones that can help heal them?
   - ○ ribs
   - ○ microscope
   - ○ living cells

4. A good title for this story is:
   - ○ Babies
   - ○ Legs
   - ○ Your Bones

F. Story Comprehension

Read the story. Then answer each question.
Fill in the bubble next to the best answer.

When astronauts go to work in space, they are too far away to come home each night. They have to live in space for a short time to do their work. But life in space is different from life on earth! The main reason is that there is less *gravity*. Gravity is the invisible force that holds everything — even you — to the earth. With less gravity, astronauts' feet don't stay on the ground, so they float instead of walk. It feels a bit like swimming. At night, astronauts sleep in sleeping bags strapped to the walls so they don't float around. To eat without pots and pans flying, astronauts have special foods that come in foil pouches. To get clean, astronauts rub soap and water on their bodies and sponge it off. That's because a shower would spray all over.

1. Why do astronauts have to live in space to do their work?
   - They are lost.
   - They are too far away to come home each night.
   - They are floating.

2. The force that holds you to the earth is called _____.
   - gravity
   - astronaut
   - foil

3. One thing an astronaut has to do in space is:
   - sleep in a sleeping bag strapped to the walls.
   - eat candy.
   - watch TV.

4. Write a sentence telling something about life in space.

   _____

   _____

Scholastic Success With

CONTEMPORARY MANUSCRIPT

Name _____

Aa

Trace and write.

A A A

a a a a

Aa

Artist Anika

asks for answers.

102 **Scholastic Success With Contemporary Manuscript • Grade 2**

Bb

Bb

Trace and write.

Baker Bobby

buys biscuits.

Cc

Trace and write.

C C C

c c c c

Cc

Cowboy Christopher

catches coyotes.

Dd

Trace and write.

D D D D

d d d d

Dd

Dancer Deandra

dances with ducks.

Ee

Trace and write.

E E E

e e e e

Ee

Engineer Eduardo

enjoys eating.

Ff

Trace and write.

Firefighter Freda

feels fearless.

Name _____

Gg

Trace and write.

G G G

g g g g

Gg

PEAS

Gardener Gloria

grows greens.

Name _____

Hh

Trace and write.

Handyman Harry

helps Hazel Hippo.

Ii

Trace and write.

Inspector Irving

is investigating.

Name _____

Jj

Trace and write.

Juggler Jeannie

jumps joyfully.

Kk

Trace and write.

King Kevin kisses

kind kittens.

Name _____

Ll

Trace and write.

Reading is fun!

Librarian Louis

loves listening.

Mm

Trace and write.

M M M M

m m m m

Mm

Musician Matt

makes merry.

Nn

Trace and write.

N N N N

n n n n

Nn

Nurse Nancy

needs new patients.

Oo

Trace and write.

Optometrist Oliver

owns one octopus.

Pp

Trace and write.

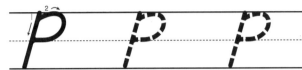

P   P   P   P

p   p   p   p   p

Pp

Postman Paul

piles packages.

Qq

Trace and write.

Q Q Q Q

q q q q

Qq

Queen Quiana

quilts quietly.

Rr

Trace and write.

 R R R

r r r r

Rr

Racer Rowena rides

rapidly to Rome.

Ss

Trace and write.

Sailor Sofia

sings sea songs.

Name _____

Tt

Tt

Trace and write.

T T T T T

t t t t t

Tt

Teacher Tatiana

tells tall tales.

Uu

Trace and write.

You're out!

Umpire Umar

upset Ursula.

Vv

Trace and write.

Veterinarian Vince

visited Victoria.

Ww

Trace and write.

Weatherman Wes

went west.

Xx

Trace and write.

Explorer Xian

is excited.

Name _____

Yy

Trace and write.

Y Y Y Y

y y y y

Yy

Yachtsman Yves

yodels loudly.

Zz

Trace and write.

Zena Zebra

zooms to the zoo.

A–Z

Trace and write.

A B C D E F G H I

J K L M N O P Q R

S T U V W X Y Z

a–z

Trace and write.

a   b   c   d   e

f   g   h   i   j   k

l   m   n   o   p

q   r   s   t   u

v   w   x   y   z

1–5

Trace and write.

6-10

Trace and write.

6 6

7 7

8 8

9 9

10 10

Colour Words

Trace and write.

red

yellow

blue

green

orange

yellow

red

blue

green

orange

Name _____

More Colour Words

Trace and write.

purple

brown

black

white

pink

pink

purple

white

brown

black

Number Words

Trace and write.

1 one

2 two

3 three

4 four

5 five

More Number Words

Trace and write.

6 six

7 seven

8 eight

9 nine

10 ten

Shapes

Trace and write.

oval

heart

circle

square

triangle

diamond

rectangle

Days of the Week

Trace and write.

Sunday

Monday

Tuesday

Wednesday

Thursday

Friday

Saturday

Months

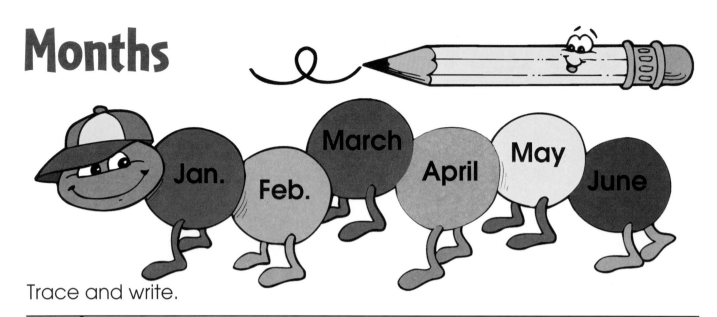

Trace and write.

January

February

March

April

May

June

Name _____

Months

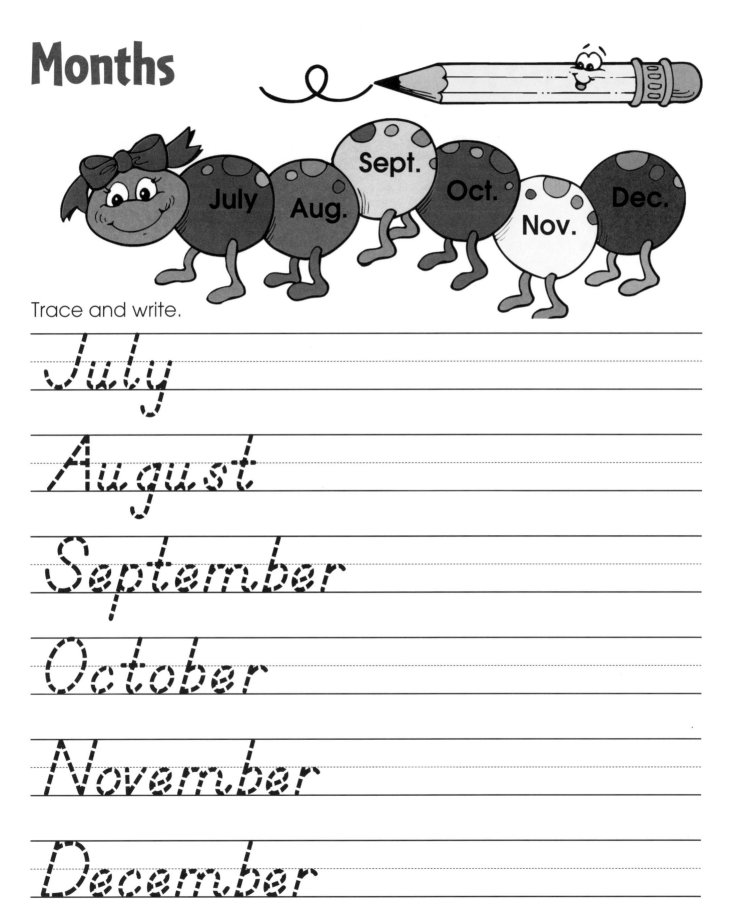

Trace and write.

July

August

September

October

November

December

Special Days

Write each special day.

JAN   FEB.   MAR.   APRIL   MAY   JUN.   JULY

New Year's Day _____

_____

_____

Valentine's Day _____

_____

_____

Mother's Day _____

_____

_____

Father's Day _____

_____

_____

National Indigenous People's Day _____

_____

_____

Canada Day _____

_____

Special Days

Write each
special day.

AUG. SEPT. OCT. NOV. DEC.

Eid-al-Adha _____
_____
_____

Thanksgiving _____
_____
_____

Halloween _____
_____
_____

Diwali _____
_____
_____

Hannukah _____
_____
_____

Christmas _____
_____
_____

Careers From A to Z

Write the career names on the lines below.

astronaut
banker
chef
doctor
engineer
firefighter
grocer
hotel worker
inspector
janitor

Name _____

Careers From A to Z

Write the career names on the lines below.

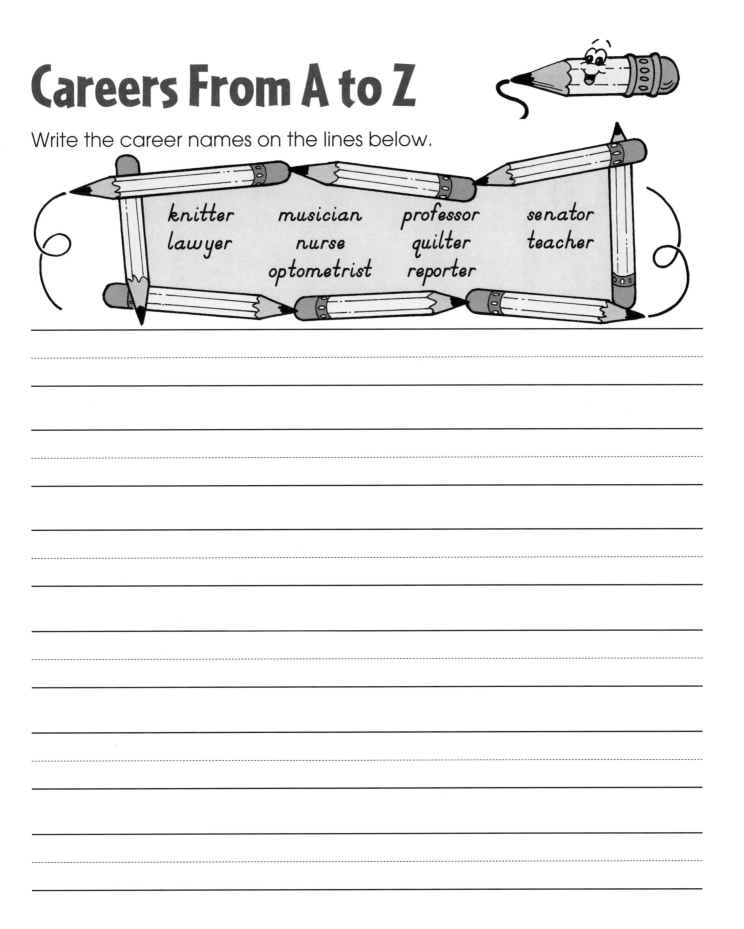

knitter musician professor senator
lawyer nurse quilter teacher
optometrist reporter

Careers From A to Z

Write the career names on the lines below.

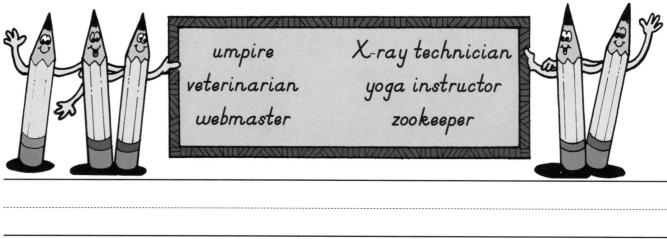

umpire   X-ray technician

veterinarian   yoga instructor

webmaster   zookeeper

The Planets

Write the names of the planets.

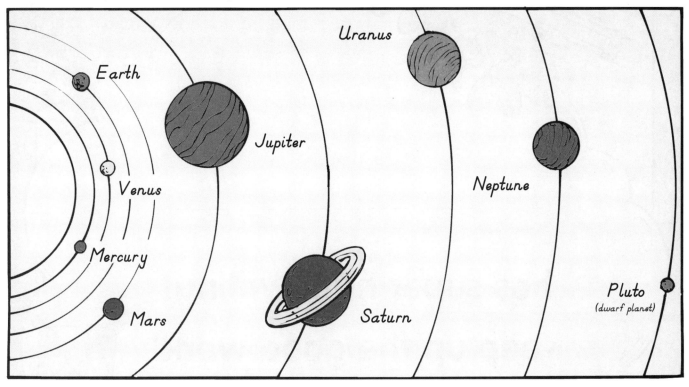

_____

_____

_____

_____

_____

_____

_____

has super handwriting!
Keep up the good work!

_____
signed

_____
date

Scholastic Success With

GRAMMAR

Telling Sentences and Questions

 *A **telling sentence** tells something. It begins with a capital letter and ends with a period. A **question** asks something. It begins with a capital letter and ends with a question mark.*

Read each sentence. Write T on the line if the sentence is a telling sentence. Write Q on the line if it is a question.

1 I took my pet to see the vet. _____

2 Was your pet sick? _____

3 What did the vet do? _____

4 The vet checked my pet. _____

5 The vet said my pet had a cold. _____

The order of the words in a sentence can change its meaning.
Write T next to the sentence that is a telling sentence.
Write Q next to the sentence that is a question.

6 Is your pet well now? _____

7 Now your pet is well. _____

Telling Sentences and Questions

*A **telling sentence** tells something. It begins with a capital letter and ends with a period.*
*A **question** asks something. It begins with a capital letter and ends with a question mark.*

Underline the capital letter that begins each sentence. Add a period (.) if it is a telling sentence. Add a question mark (?) if it is a question.

1 The vet is nice _____

2 She helped my dog _____

3 Did she see your cat _____

4 Is the cat well now _____

5 My cat feels better _____

The order of the words in a sentence can change its meaning. Change the word order in the telling sentence to make it a question. Write the question.

6 He will take the cat home.

_____

Telling Sentences and Questions

Look at the underlined part of each sentence. If it is written correctly, fill in the last bubble. If not, fill in the bubble next to the correct answer.

1 The girl likes dogs.
- ⬭ the girl
- ⬭ Girl the
- ⬭ correct as is

2 the vet helps sick pets.
- ⬭ the Vet
- ⬭ The vet
- ⬭ correct as is

3 The boy likes cats?
- ⬭ cats.
- ⬭ cats
- ⬭ correct as is

4 Is the vet nice?
- ⬭ nice
- ⬭ nice.
- ⬭ correct as is

5 do you have a pet?
- ⬭ Do You
- ⬭ Do you
- ⬭ correct as is

6 Is when the vet open?
- ⬭ When is
- ⬭ when Is
- ⬭ correct as is

7 he has a bird.
- ⬭ Has he
- ⬭ He has
- ⬭ correct as is

8 My dog likes the vet?
- ⬭ The vet.
- ⬭ the vet.
- ⬭ correct as is

9 Who has a goldfish.
- ⬭ goldfish?
- ⬭ goldfish
- ⬭ correct as is

10 will you see the vet again?
- ⬭ Will you
- ⬭ You
- ⬭ correct as is

Exclamations and Commands

 An **exclamation** shows strong feelings, such as excitement, surprise, or fear. It begins with a capital letter and ends with an exclamation mark (!).

A **command** makes a request or tells someone to do something. It ends with a period or an exclamation mark.

Read each sentence. Write **E** if the sentence is an exclamation. Write **C** if the sentence is a command.

1 Ruby copies Angela!   ———

2 Look at their dresses.   ———

3 They're exactly the same!   ———

4 Angela is mad!   ———

5 Look at Ruby!   ———

6 Show Angela how Ruby hops. ———

Write each sentence correctly.

Exclamation i'm upset

7
_____

Command don't copy other people

8
_____

Exclamations and Commands

An **exclamation** *shows strong feelings, such as excitement, surprise, or fear. It begins with a capital letter and ends with an exclamation mark (!).*

A **command** *makes a request or tells someone to do something. It ends with a period or an exclamation mark.*

Read each exclamation. Use words from the box to tell what strong feeling it shows.

excitement	fear	anger	surprise

1 I lost my jacket. I'll be so cold! _____

2 Look what I have! _____

3 I didn't know you had my jacket! _____

4 Give it to me now! _____

Look at the picture.

5 Circle the command that goes with the picture.

Please don't be upset!   Wear your new hat.

6 Write another command for the picture.

_____

7 Write an exclamation for the picture.

_____

Exclamations and Commands

Read each exclamation. If it is written correctly, fill in the last bubble.
If not, fill in the bubble next to the correct way to write it.

1 You are a great hopper

○ You are a great hopper!

○ You are a great hopper.

○ You are a greathopper!

○ correct as is

2 the picture looks beautiful.

○ The picture looks beautiful!

○ The picture looks beautiful

○ the picture looks beautiful!

○ correct as is

3 i can paint, too!

○ i can paint, too

○ I can paint, too!

○ I can paint, too

○ correct as is

4 I did it!

○ i did it!

○ I did it

○ i did it

○ correct as is

Read each command. If it is written correctly, fill in the last bubble.
If not, fill in the bubble next to the correct way to write it.

5 teach me how to hop.

○ teach me how to hop

○ Teach me how to hop

○ Teach me how to hop.

○ correct as is

6 Hop backward like this

○ Hop backward like this.

○ hop backward like this

○ hop backward like this!

○ correct as is

Types of Sentences; Capital I

A **telling sentence** begins with a capital letter and ends with a period. A question begins with a capital letter and ends with a question mark. An **exclamation** begins with a capital letter and ends with an exclamation mark. A **command** begins with a capital letter and ends with a period. The word **I** is always capitalized in a sentence.

Read each sentence. Circle the beginning letter, end punctuation, and the word I in each sentence.

1 I sail my boat in the lake.

2 May I have a turn?

3 I am so happy!

4 Can Kiku and I play?

5 Bill and I fly the kite.

Write each sentence in the correct box.

Telling Sentences

_____

_____

Questions

_____

_____

Exclamation _____

Types of Sentences; Capital I

*A **telling sentence** begins with a capital letter and ends with a period. A **question** begins with a capital letter and ends with a question mark. An **exclamation** begins with a capital letter and ends with an exclamation mark. A **command** begins with a capital letter and ends with a period. The word **I** is always capitalized in a sentence.*

Decide if each sentence is a telling sentence, a question, an exclamation,or a command. Write T, Q, E, or C on the lines.

1 My sister and I went to the lake. _____

2 Come see this. _____

3 I saw three little sailboats. _____

4 Put the boat in the water. _____

5 Did I have a good time? _____

6 You bet! I loved it! _____

7 Can I go again soon? _____

What would you do at the lake? Use the word I and your own ideas to finish the sentences.

8 At the lake _____ saw _____ .

9 _____ can _____ .

10 My friend and _____ liked _____ best.

Types of Sentences; Capital I

Read each sentence. If it is written correctly, fill in the last bubble. If not, fill in the bubble next to the correct way to write it.

1 i have fun with my bike.

- ◯ I have fun with my bike.
- ◯ I have fun with my bike
- ◯ i have fun with my bike
- ◯ correct as is

2 can I ride to the beach

- ◯ Can I ride to the beach
- ◯ Can I ride to the beach?
- ◯ Can i ride to the beach?
- ◯ correct as is

3 i find a pretty shell

- ◯ I find a pretty shell
- ◯ i find a pretty shell.
- ◯ I find a pretty shell.
- ◯ correct as is

4 Jill and I see a crab.

- ◯ Jill and I see a crab
- ◯ Jill and i see a crab.
- ◯ Jill and i see a crab
- ◯ correct as is

5 get the shovel

- ◯ Get the shovel
- ◯ Get the shovel.
- ◯ get the shovel.
- ◯ correct as is

6 what a mess I made

- ◯ What a mess I made!
- ◯ What a mess I made
- ◯ what a mess I made!
- ◯ correct as is

Common Nouns

 Common nouns *name people, places, or things.*

Read each sentence. Circle the common nouns.

1 The boy made a boat.

2 The brothers went to the park.

3 A girl was with her grandmother.

4 Two boats crashed in the lake.

5 Friends used a needle and thread to fix the sail.

Write the common nouns you circled under the correct heading below.

People	Places	Things
_____	_____	_____
_____	_____	_____
_____		_____
_____		_____
_____		_____

Common Nouns

Common nouns *name people, places, or things.*

Help sort the cards. Some of the words are nouns. Some are not.
Circle the nouns.

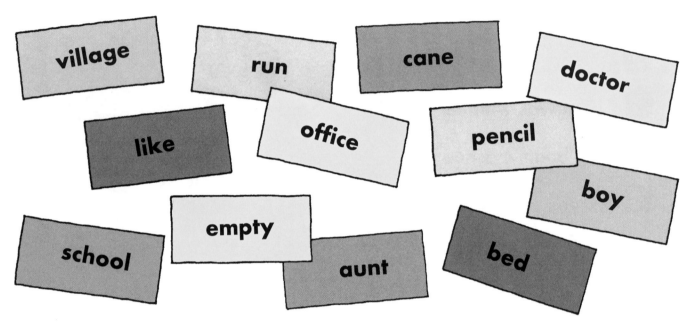

village   run   cane   doctor   like   office   pencil   boy   school   empty   aunt   bed

Write each noun you circled under the correct heading.

People	Place	Thing

Common Nouns

Look at the underlined word in each sentence. If it is a common noun, fill in the bubble next to yes. If it is not a common noun, fill in the bubble next to no.

1 Our class <u>went</u> on a trip.

    ○ yes   ○ no

2 We went to the <u>city.</u>

    ○ yes   ○ no

3 The buildings were <u>tall.</u>

    ○ yes   ○ no

4 There were many <u>cars.</u>

    ○ yes   ○ no

A common noun is underlined in each sentence. Tell if it names a person, place or thing. Fill in the bubble next to the correct answer.

5 We went into a big <u>room.</u>

    ○ person   ○ place   ○ thing

6 Our <u>teacher</u> led us.

    ○ person   ○ place   ○ thing

7 I walked with my best <u>friend.</u>

    ○ person   ○ place   ○ thing

8 We sat at a long <u>table.</u>

    ○ person   ○ place   ○ thing

Capitalize Names and Places

 Special names of people and places always begin with capital letters. They are called **proper nouns**.

Read each sentence. Circle the proper noun.

1 George Ancona is a photographer.

2 He was born in Mexico.

3 His family called him Jorgito.

4 They lived in Vancouver.

5 Now he travels to Honduras to take pictures.

6 Tio Mario worked in a sign shop.

Write the proper nouns you circled under the correct heading below.

People

_____

_____

_____

Places

_____

_____

_____

Capitalize Names and Places

Special names of people and places always begin with capital letters. They are called **proper nouns**.

Read the postcard. Find the proper nouns. Write them correctly on the lines below.

Dear sue,

It's very hot here in california. We visited the city of los angeles. Then we swam in the pacific ocean. I miss you.

Love,

tonya

sue wong
11 shore road
victoria, BC

1 _____ **2** _____

3 _____ **4** _____

5 _____ **6** _____

7 _____ **8** _____

Write a sentence with a proper noun. Underline the capital letter or letters in the proper noun. Then write whether it names a person or a place.

_____

_____

Capitalize Names and Places

A proper noun is underlined in each sentence. Does it name a person or a place? Fill in the bubble next to the correct answer.

1 <u>Betty</u> is a photographer.

◯ person   ◯ place

2 She goes to <u>Nova</u> <u>Scotia</u> to take pictures.

◯ person   ◯ place

3 She meets her older brother <u>Peter</u>.

◯ person   ◯ place

4 She takes his picture in a city called <u>Halifax</u>.

◯ person   ◯ place

Read each sentence. Find the proper noun. Fill in the bubble next to the word that is a proper noun.

5 Their friend is Emilio.

◯ friend   ◯ Emilio

◯ Their   ◯ is

6 They all went to Florida.

◯ Florida   ◯ all

◯ They   ◯ went

7 They visited Disney World there.

◯ They

◯ there

◯ visited

◯ Disney World

8 They walked down Main Street in the park.

◯ park

◯ walked

◯ They

◯ Main Street

Verbs

*A **verb** is an action word. It tells what someone or something is doing.*

Read each sentence. Write the action verb in the telling part of the sentence.

1 Ronald runs to the field. _____

2 Michael wears a batting helmet. _____

3 He smacks the ball hard. _____

4 Ronald holds the wrong end
of the bat. _____

5 He misses the ball. _____

6 Ronald waits in left field. _____

7 He writes G for great. _____

8 Ronald's father helps him. _____

Write a sentence about the picture.
Use an action verb and circle it.

_____

_____

_____

Verbs

 *A **verb** is an action word. It tells what someone or something is doing.*

Draw a line to match each sentence with an action verb. Then write the action verbs on the lines to finish the sentences.

1 Moms and dads _____ the game.   throws

2 The pitcher _____ the ball.   opens

3 Ronald _____ his eyes.   watch

4 The team _____ for Ronald.   cheers

5 Ronald _____ the ball past the pitcher.   runs

6 He _____ to first base.   hits

7 Someone _____, "Go Ronald go!"   eat

8 The kids _____ ice cream after the game.   yells

Verbs

Look at the underlined word in each sentence. Fill in the correct bubble to tell whether or not it is an action verb.

1 The dog <u>runs</u> down the road.
- ⬭ action verb
- ⬭ not an action verb

2 The <u>girl</u> chases the dog.
- ⬭ action verb
- ⬭ not an action verb

3 The dog finds a <u>bone</u>.
- ⬭ action verb
- ⬭ not an action verb

4 The <u>sun</u> sets.
- ⬭ action verb
- ⬭ not an action verb

5 Rain <u>falls</u> from the sky.
- ⬭ action verb
- ⬭ not an action verb

6 The girl <u>splashes</u> water.
- ⬭ action verb
- ⬭ not an action verb

7 The dog hides under a <u>bush</u>.
- ⬭ action verb
- ⬭ not an action verb

8 The girl <u>finds</u> the dog.
- ⬭ action verb
- ⬭ not an action verb

9 The sun <u>shines</u>.
- ⬭ action verb
- ⬭ not an action verb

10 The girl sees a <u>rainbow</u>.
- ⬭ action verb
- ⬭ not an action verb

Name _____

Simple Sentences

 *A **simple sentence** has a naming part and a telling part. It tells a complete thought.*

 Read each group of words. Put an X next to it if it is a complete thought. Circle the naming part and underline the telling part in each sentence.

1 One day thirsty   _____

2 Crow could not get a drink.   _____

3 The water rose.   _____

4 The old mouse   _____

5 Put the bell   _____

6 One mouse had a plan.   _____

Write a simple sentence about the picture below.
Circle the naming part and underline the telling part.

_____

Simple Sentences

 *A **simple sentence** has a naming part and a telling part. It tells a complete thought.*

Circle the sentence in each pair. Then underline the naming part of the sentence.

1 (a) Lin likes to play soccer.

   (b) likes to play soccer

2 (a) Her friends

   (b) Her friends watch her play.

3 (a) They cheer for Lin.

   (b) They cheer for

4 (a) Her mom goes to all of her games.

   (b) goes to all of her games

5 (a) The coach is very proud of Lin.

   (b) The coach is

Simple Sentences

Read each sentence. Fill in the bubble to tell if the underlined words are the naming or the telling part of the sentence. Some of the underlined words may not be the whole part.

1 The cat was under the tree.
- ○ naming part
- ○ telling part
- ○ not the whole part

2 A bird saw the cat.
- ○ naming part
- ○ telling part
- ○ not the whole part

3 The bird flew away.
- ○ naming part
- ○ telling part
- ○ not the whole part

4 Then, the cat walked away.
- ○ naming part
- ○ telling part
- ○ not the whole part

Fill in the bubble to choose a naming or telling part that makes a sentence.

5 The bird ____.
- ○ in the tall tree
- ○ saw the cat go away
- ○ flying very fast in the sky

6 ____ came back to the tree.
- ○ Deep in the woods
- ○ The large and pretty
- ○ Then the bird

7 ____ saw the bird.
- ○ After a minute, the cat
- ○ Running across the grass
- ○ The cat was watching

8 So the cat ____.
- ○ walking to the tree
- ○ under the tree
- ○ walked back, too

Past-Tense Verbs

 *Some verbs add **-ed** to tell about actions that happened in the past.*

Find the past-tense verb in each sentence. Write it on the line.

1 Last spring, Daisy planted a garden. _____

2 Floyd watered the garden. _____

3 Together they weeded their garden. _____

4 One day they discovered a big carrot. _____

Read each sentence. If the sentence has a past-tense verb, write it on the line. If the sentence does not have a past-tense verb, leave the line blank.

5 They like to eat carrots. _____

6 They pulled on the carrot. _____

Past-Tense Verbs

 *Some verbs add **-ed** to tell about actions that happened in the past.*

Read the first sentence in each pair. Change the underlined verb to tell about the past.

1 Today my dogs <u>push</u> open the back door.

Yesterday my dogs _____ open the back door.

2 Today they <u>splash</u> in the rain puddles.

Last night they _____ in the rain puddles.

3 Now they <u>roll</u> in the mud.

Last week they _____ in the mud.

4 Today I <u>follow</u> my dogs' footprints.

Last Sunday I _____ my dogs' footprints.

5 Now I <u>wash</u> my dogs from head to toe.

Earlier I _____ my dogs from head to toe.

Write a sentence using one of the verbs you wrote.

_____

_____

_____

Past-Tense Verbs

Read each sentence. Look at the underlined verb. If it is not correct, fill in the bubble next to the correct verb. If it is correct, fill in the last bubble.

1 Last Saturday I <u>visit</u> John in the country.
○ visited
○ correct as is

2 Two weeks ago we <u>watched</u> a sailboat race.
○ watch
○ correct as is

3 A week ago we <u>walked</u> to the top of a big hill.
○ walk
○ correct as is

4 Last week I <u>talk</u> to John on the phone.
○ talked
○ correct as is

5 Earlier I <u>ask</u> him to visit me in the city.
○ asked
○ correct as is

6 Friday morning his train <u>pulled</u> into the station.
○ pull
○ correct as is

7 Last night my dog <u>barked</u> when he saw John.
○ bark
○ correct as is

8 Yesterday I <u>show</u> John around the city.
○ showed
○ correct as is

Pronouns

 *A **pronoun** takes the place of the name of a person, place, or thing.*

Read each pair of sentences. Circle the pronoun in the second sentence of each pair. Then write what the pronoun stands for. The first one has been done for you.

1 Wendell did not like to clean his room.

(He) liked a messy room.   Wendell
_____

2 Mother wanted Wendell to do some work.

She handed Wendell a broom.   _____

3 The pigs came into Wendell's room.

They helped Wendell clean the room.   _____

4 Wendell and the pigs played a board game.

Wendell and the pigs had fun playing it.   _____

5 The pigs and Wendell played for a long time.

They liked to play games.   _____

6 Wendell was sad to see his friends go.

He liked playing with the pigs.   _____

Pronouns

 *A **pronoun** takes the place of the name of a person, place, or thing.*

Read the story. Use the pronouns in the box to complete each sentence. The first one has been done for you.

they he she it

Emma was walking in the woods. At last ___she___

came to a house. _____ was empty. She opened the door
1

and saw three chairs by the fireplace. _____ were all
2

different sizes. She sat down on the smallest one. _____
3

was the perfect size for her. Soon _____ fell asleep.
4

When she woke up, three pigs were

standing over her. The father pig spoke. _____
5

asked Emma if she would stay for dinner. "I would love to!"

said Emma.

Pronouns

Read each sentence. Fill in the bubble next to the word or words that the underlined pronoun stands for.

1 <u>She</u> did not like the mess.
- ○ Wendell
- ○ The boy
- ○ The pigs
- ○ Mrs. Fultz

2 <u>He</u> did not like brooms.
- ○ The pigs
- ○ The boys
- ○ The boy
- ○ Mrs. Fultz

3 <u>It</u> was full of pigs.
- ○ The rooms
- ○ The house
- ○ The pigs
- ○ The door

4 <u>They</u> wanted to play.
- ○ The room
- ○ Wendell
- ○ The pigs
- ○ Mrs. Fultz

Read each sentence. Fill in the bubble next to the pronoun that can take the place of the underlined word or words.

5 <u>Wendell</u> waved good-bye to the pigs.
- ○ He
- ○ She
- ○ It
- ○ They

6 Wendell hoped <u>the pigs</u> would come back.
- ○ it
- ○ he
- ○ they
- ○ she

Types of Sentences

 *A **telling sentence** tells something. A **question** asks something. An **exclamation** shows strong feelings. A **command** makes a request or gives a command.*

Read each sentence. Write it next to the correct heading.

What a big mango!	I like mangoes.
Is that a banana?	Did you find the fruit?
Buy me an avocado.	Come over for dinner.
I want to eat dinner.	This tastes great!

Exclamation: _____

_____

Command: _____

_____

Question: _____

_____

Telling Sentence: _____

_____

Types of Sentences

A **telling sentence** *tells something.* A **question** *asks something.* An **exclamation** *shows strong feelings.* A command *makes a request or gives a command.*

Read the following sentences. Write the correct end punctuation mark for each sentence. Then write the sentence type on the line to the right of each sentence. Write T for each telling sentence or statement, Q for each question, E for each exclamation, and C for each command.

1 We're going to the beach __ _____

2 Do you have your bathing suit __ _____

3 We will play in the sand __ _____

4 Pack the sunscreen __ _____

5 I love swimming __ _____

6 Take the beach chair __ _____

7 What time do we leave __ _____

8 Wow, that's a huge wave __ _____

Types of Sentences

Read each sentence. Fill in the bubble next to the correct type of sentence.

1 Give me that apple.

○ telling   ○ question   ○ exclamation   ○ command

2 What kind of fruit is this?

○ telling   ○ question   ○ exclamation   ○ command

3 What a great dinner!

○ telling   ○ question   ○ exclamation   ○ command

4 Buy this watermelon.

○ telling   ○ question   ○ exclamation   ○ command

5 This is the best watermelon!

○ telling   ○ question   ○ exclamation   ○ command

6 I would like to have another piece.

○ telling   ○ question   ○ exclamation   ○ command

7 Are those bananas ripe?

○ telling   ○ question   ○ exclamation   ○ command

8 A mango is smaller than a watermelon.

○ telling   ○ question   ○ exclamation   ○ command

Word Order

Words in a sentence must be in an order that makes sense.

Read each group of words. Write the words in the correct order to make a statement. Begin each statement with a capital letter and end it with a period.

1 brothers two can live together

_____

2 Hungbu find will a home new

_____

3 will fix Mother the house

_____

Read each group of words. Write the words in the correct order to make a question. Begin each question with a capital letter and end it with a question mark.

4 clean Sister will house the

_____

5 help can the bird them

_____

Word Order

 Words in a sentence must be in an order that makes sense.

Write the words in the correct order to make a sentence. Then write if the sentence is a question or a statement.

1 find Will I some wood? _____

_____

2 must Each of help us. _____

_____

3 trees are the Where? _____

_____

Write each group of words in the correct order to make a statement. Then write them in the correct order to make a question. Add capital letters and end punctuation to your sentences.

4 your pumpkin is that _____

_____

5 help cut you can pumpkin the _____

_____

Word Order

Read each group of words. If the word order does not make sense, fill in the bubble next to the correct word order. If the words are in an order that makes sense, fill in the last bubble.

1 Dad made breakfast for eggs.
- ○ Made for breakfast Dad eggs.
- ○ Dad made breakfast eggs for.
- ○ Dad made eggs for breakfast.
- ○ correct as is

2 Open eggs four he cracked.
- ○ He cracked eggs open four.
- ○ He cracked open four eggs.
- ○ Four eggs cracked open he.
- ○ correct as is

3 Like do eggs you?
- ○ Eggs do you like?
- ○ Do you like eggs?
- ○ Do eggs like you?
- ○ correct as is

4 Help did you him?
- ○ Did help you him?
- ○ Did you help him?
- ○ Help you did him?
- ○ correct as is

5 With fork a beat eggs.
- ○ Beat eggs with a fork.
- ○ Eggs beat a fork with.
- ○ A fork beat with eggs.
- ○ correct as is

6 Do you want some toast?
- ○ Do you toast some want?
- ○ Do some toast want you?
- ○ You want do some toast?
- ○ correct as is

Plural Nouns

*Most nouns add **-s** to mean more than one. Nouns that end in **s**, **x**, **ch**, or **sh** add **-es** to mean more than one.*

Read the sentences. Underline the plural nouns. Circle the letter or letters that were added to mean more than one.

1 We have two accordions in our house.

2 Grandma has many brushes to fix her hair.

3 My grandfather has many clocks and watches.

4 A lot of flowers are in the boxes.

Write the nouns that add -s.

_____

Write the nouns that add -es.

_____

Name _____

Plural Nouns

 *Most nouns add **-s** to mean more than one. Nouns that end in **s**, **x**, **ch**, or **sh** add **-es** to mean more than one.*

Read each sentence. Add -s or -es to the noun at the end of the sentence to make it plural. Write it in the sentence.

1 Dad made five cheese _____. (sandwich)

2 He packed five _____ for the children. (lunch)

3 Lisa put fruit in all the _____. (lunchbox)

4 She packed some paper _____, **too.** (dish)

Write the plural for each noun on the line.

5 one box

two _____

6 one dress

two _____

7 one coat

two _____

8 one bench

two _____

Plural Nouns

Read each pair of nouns. If the plural noun is correct, fill in the last bubble. If it is not correct, fill in the bubble next to the correct plural noun.

1 sketch, sketchs
  ○ sketches
  ○ correct as is

2 tree, trees
  ○ treess
  ○ correct as is

3 fox, foxs
  ○ foxes
  ○ correct as is

4 paint, paints
  ○ paintes
  ○ correct as is

5 squirrel, squirrels
  ○ squirreles
  ○ correct as is

6 dress, dressees
  ○ dresses
  ○ correct as is

7 ball, balles
  ○ balls
  ○ correct as is

8 wish, wishes
  ○ wishs
  ○ correct as is

Adjectives

 *An **adjective** describes a person, place, or thing. Colour, size, and number words are adjectives.*

Read each sentence. Underline the nouns. Write the adjective that tells about each noun.

1 The brown donkey carried the heavy

_____   _____

2 The striped cat chased two birds.

_____   _____

3 The little rooster crowed six times.

_____   _____

Write the adjectives from the sentences above.

4 Write the adjectives that tell what kind.

_____

5 Write the adjectives that tell how many.

_____

Adjectives

 *An **adjective** describes a person, place, or thing. Colour, size, and number words are adjectives.*

Read each sentence. Find the adjective and the noun it describes.
Circle the noun. Write the adjective on the line.

1 Peggy and Rosa went to the big zoo.   _____

2 They looked up at the tall giraffe.   _____

3 The giraffe looked down at the two girls.   _____

4 The giraffe had brown spots.   _____

Write adjectives from the sentences in the chart.

Colour Word	Size Words	Number Word
_____	_____	_____
	_____	

Adjectives

Read each sentence. Fill in the bubble next to the word that is an adjective.

1 In the morning, Jenny put on red boots.

- ○ put
- ○ boots
- ○ red
- ○ on

2 She found a yellow hat in the closet.

- ○ She
- ○ hat
- ○ found
- ○ yellow

3 She opened her purple umbrella.

- ○ opened
- ○ She
- ○ umbrella
- ○ purple

4 Jenny walked past a big house.

- ○ big
- ○ house
- ○ walked
- ○ past

5 She waved to three friends.

- ○ waved
- ○ three
- ○ to
- ○ friends

6 A little puppy trotted behind her.

- ○ trotted
- ○ puppy
- ○ little
- ○ behind

7 She jumped over a huge puddle.

- ○ She
- ○ jumped
- ○ huge
- ○ puddle

8 Two birds took a drink of water.

- ○ birds
- ○ of
- ○ took
- ○ Two

Verb to be

Am, **is, are**, **was**, and **were** are forms of the verb **to be**. These verbs show being instead of action.

Read each sentence. Underline the verb. Write past if the sentence tells about the past. Write now if the sentence tells about the present.

1 The story is perfect.   _____

2 The producers are happy.   _____

3 The actors were funny.   _____

4 The movie studio is interested in the story.   _____

5 I am excited about the movie.   _____

6 I was sad at the end.   _____

Verb to be

 Am, **is**, **are**, **was**, and **were** are forms of the verb **to be**. These verbs show being instead of action.

Choose a verb from the box to finish each sentence. There may be more than one right answer. Write one if the sentence tells about one. Write more if it tells about more than one.

am	is	are	was	were

1 The movie _____ long. _____

2 She _____ in the movie. _____

3 They _____ at the movie theatre yesterday. _____

4 The producers _____ spending money now. _____

5 The director _____ not at work yesterday. _____

6 The actors _____ acting now. _____

Verb to be

Read each sentence. Fill in the bubble next to the words that correctly tell about the sentence.

1 The movie was very long
- ○ past, more than one
- ○ present, more than one
- ○ past, one
- ○ present, one

2 The seats at the movies are high up.
- ○ past, more than one
- ○ present, more than one
- ○ past, one
- ○ present, one

3 The actors were all big stars.
- ○ past, more than one
- ○ present, more than one
- ○ past, one
- ○ present, one

4 The scenes were interesting.
- ○ past, more than one
- ○ present, more than one
- ○ past, one
- ○ present, one

5 The trees and flowers were so beautiful.
- ○ past, more than one
- ○ present, more than one
- ○ past, one
- ○ present, one

6 I am going to see the movie again.
- ○ past, more than one
- ○ present, more than one
- ○ past, one
- ○ present, one

Irregular Verbs go, do

Irregular verbs change their spelling when they tell about the past. **Did** *is the past form of* **do** *and* **does**. **Went** *is the past form of* **go** *and* **goes**.

Read each sentence. Write present if the underlined verb tells about action now. Write past if it tells about action in the past.

Present	Past
go, goes	went
do, does	did

1 Grace goes to the playground. _____

2 Some other children go, too. _____

3 Grace does a scene from a story. _____

4 The children do the scene with her. _____

5 Grace went into battle as Joan of Arc. _____

6 She did the part of Anansi the Spider, too. _____

7 In another part, Grace went inside a

wooden horse. _____

8 She did many other parts. _____

Irregular Verbs go, do

 Irregular verbs change their spelling when they tell about the past. **Did** *is the past form of* **do** *and* **does.** **Went** *is the past form of* **go** *and* **goes**.

Choose the correct word from the chart and write it on the line.

In the Present	In the Past
go, goes	went
do, does	did

1 Last week our family _____ to the art museum.

2 Pablo _____ there a lot.

3 His mother _____ the displays there now.

4 She _____ a new one yesterday.

5 _____ you want to join us tomorrow?

6 We want to _____ after lunch again.

Irregular Verbs go, do

Fill in the bubble next to the word that correctly completes the sentence.

1 Rose ____ to the ballet.
- ○ go
- ○ did
- ○ goes

2 Two dancers ____ a kick and a turn.
- ○ do
- ○ does
- ○ goes

3 Another dancer ____ a hop and a jump.
- ○ went
- ○ does
- ○ do

4 They ____ around in circles very fast.
- ○ goes
- ○ did
- ○ go

5 A girl ____ two big splits.
- ○ do
- ○ did
- ○ went

6 Then she ____ off stage.
- ○ go
- ○ did
- ○ went

7 Rose ____ home feeling very happy.
- ○ went
- ○ did
- ○ go

8 She ____ some of the steps, too.
- ○ do
- ○ did
- ○ goes

Quotation Marks

Quotation marks *show the exact words someone says. They go before the speaker's first word. They also go after the speaker's last word and the end punctuation mark.*

Read each sentence. Underline the exact words the speaker says. Put the words in quotation marks. The first one is done for you.

1 Max said, "Let's go on a picnic."

2 Cori replied, That's a great idea.

3 Andy asked, What should we bring?

4 Max said with a laugh, We should bring food.

5 Cori added, Yes, let's bring lots and lots of food.

6 Andy giggled and said, You're no help at all!

Finish the sentences below by writing what Max, Cori, and Andy might say next. Use quotation marks.

7 Max said, _____ .

8 Cori asked, _____ .

9 Andy answered, _____ .

Quotation Marks

Quotation marks *show the exact words someone says. They go before the speaker's first word. They also go after the speaker's last word and the end punctuation mark.*

Read the sentences. Then put quotation marks where they belong. The first one has been done for you.

1 Jan cried, "It is raining!"

2 She asked, What will we do today?

3 Tomas answered, We could read.

4 Tomas whispered, Maybe the sun will come out soon.

5 Jan whined, But what will we do now?

6 Tomas said, Use your imagination!

Finish the sentence below. Use quotation marks to show what Jan asked.

Jan asked, _____

_____

Quotation Marks

Fill in the bubble next to the correct way to write the sentence.

1
- ○ Let's make a sand castle, said Lenny.
- ○ "Let's make a sand castle, said Lenny.
- ○ "Let's make a sand castle," said Lenny.

2
- ○ Where's the pail and shovel?" asked Sonya.
- ○ "Where's the pail and shovel?" asked Sonya.
- ○ Where's the pail and shovel? asked Sonya

3
- ○ Sara said, "Maybe Otis can help."
- ○ Sara said, Maybe Otis can help."
- ○ Sara said, "Maybe Otis can help.

4
- ○ Do you want to dig? asked Lenny.
- ○ "Do you want to dig? asked Lenny.
- ○ "Do you want to dig?" asked Lenny.

5
- ○ Sonya shouted, Get some water!
- ○ Sonya shouted, "Get some water!
- ○ Sonya shouted, "Get some water!"

6
- ○ Look what we made! cried the children.
- ○ "Look what we made!" cried the children.
- ○ Look what we made!" cried the children.

Contractions With not

A **contraction** *is two words made into one word. An apostrophe takes the place of the missing letter or letters. In a contraction,* **not** *becomes* **n't***.*

Read each sentence. Underline the contraction. Write the two words the contraction is made from.

1 The little old man and little old woman aren't ready.   _____

2 The Gingerbread Man doesn't want to be eaten.   _____

3 They can't catch him.   _____

4 They couldn't run fast enough.   _____

5 He didn't come back.   _____

6 The Gingerbread Man isn't afraid of the fox.   _____

Draw a line to match each contraction to the two words it is made from.

7 hadn't   were not

8 don't   had not

9 weren't   do not

Contractions With not

*A **contraction** is two words made into one word. An apostrophe takes the place of the missing letter or letters. In a contraction, **not** becomes **n't**.*

Read each sentence. Write a contraction for the underlined words.

1 Cindy and Ed <u>could not</u> bake a cake. _____

2 There <u>was not</u> enough flour. _____

3 They <u>are not</u> happy. _____

4 They <u>cannot</u> surprise José. _____

5 <u>Do not</u> give up. _____

6 They <u>did not</u> give up.
They made cupcakes! _____

Write a sentence using a contraction you wrote.

_____

_____

Contractions With not

Fill in the bubble next to the contraction that correctly completes the sentence.

1 Our players ____ as big as theirs.
- ◯ doesn't
- ◯ haven't
- ◯ aren't

2 Our coach ____ worried.
- ◯ isn't
- ◯ didn't
- ◯ can't

3 They ____ run as fast as we can.
- ◯ weren't
- ◯ can't
- ◯ wasn't

4 Their runner ____ tag first base.
- ◯ doesn't
- ◯ haven't
- ◯ isn't

5 Their hitters ____ hit the ball hard.
- ◯ isn't
- ◯ weren't
- ◯ don't

6 Our hitters ____ miss any balls.
- ◯ doesn't
- ◯ didn't
- ◯ aren't

7 The other players ____ catch our balls.
- ◯ couldn't
- ◯ haven't
- ◯ isn't

8 They ____ ready for us.
- ◯ don't
- ◯ hadn't
- ◯ weren't

Subject/Verb Agreement

*If the naming part of a sentence names one, add **-s** to the action word. If the naming part names more than one, do not add **-s** to the action word.*

Read each sentence. Underline the word in parentheses ( ) that correctly completes it. Write the word on the line.

1 Kim _____ a story about a monkey. (write, writes)

2 The monkey _____ his friend in the city. (meet, meets)

3 The two friends _____ on the bus. (ride, rides)

4 The monkeys _____ for toys and presents. (shop, shops)

5 The store _____ at 7 o'clock. (close, closes)

6 The monkeys _____ the time. (forget, forgets)

7 The owner _____ the door. (lock, locks)

8 The friends _____ on the window. (bang, bangs)

9 Many people _____ for help. (call, calls)

10 Finally the monkeys _____ the door open. (hear, hears)

Subject/Verb Agreement

If the naming part of a sentence names one, add **-s** *to the action word. If the naming part names more than one, do not add* **-s** *to the action word.*

Read each sentence. Circle the action word in parentheses ( ) that correctly completes the sentence.

1 Two baby llamas (play/plays) in the mountains.

2 One baby llama (hide/hides) under a bush.

3 The baby animals (chase/chases) flying leaves.

4 Soon the mother llama (call/calls) them.

5 The babies (run/runs) to her.

6 The two babies (stand/stands) next to their mother.

7 One baby (close/closes) its eyes.

8 The mother llama (nudge/nudges) the baby gently.

9 But the baby llama (sleep/sleeps).

10 Soon both baby llamas (sleep/sleeps).

Subject/Verb Agreement

Fill in the bubble next to the word that correctly completes the sentence.

1 Two friends ____ beautiful bead necklaces.
○ make   ○ makes

2 One girl ____ some pieces of string.
○ cut   ○ cuts

3 The girls ____ red, blue, and yellow beads.
○ use   ○ uses

4 The yellow beads ____ in the dark.
○ glow   ○ glows

5 The necklaces ____ from the rod.
○ hang   ○ hangs

6 The boys ____ a necklace for their mother.
○ buy   ○ buys

7 One boy ____ the short necklace with round beads.
○ pick   ○ picks

8 The other boy ____ the necklace with square beads.
○ pick   ○ picks

9 Two sisters ____ the same red necklace.
○ wear   ○ wears

10 The girls ____ all the necklaces.
○ sell   ○ sells

More About Subject/Verb Agreement

If the naming part of a sentence is a noun or pronoun that names one, the verb ends in **s**, *except for the pronouns* **I** *and* **you**. *If the naming part is a noun or pronoun that names more than one, the verb does not end in* **-s**.

Read each sentence. Circle the correct verb to complete it.

1 John and his family (camp, camps) in the woods.

2 Alice (like, likes) hiking the best.

3 John (walk, walks) ahead of everyone.

4 Mom and John (build, builds) a campfire.

5 Dad and Alice (cook, cooks) dinner over the fire.

6 Alice and Mom (crawl, crawls) into the tent.

Choose two of the verbs you circled. Write a sentence using each verb.

_____

_____

Name _____

More About Subject/Verb Agreement

*If the naming part of a sentence is a noun or pronoun that names one, the verb ends in **-s**, except for the pronouns **I** and **you**. If the naming part is a noun or pronoun that names more than one, the verb does not end in **-s**.*

Choose the correct action word from the box to complete each sentence. Write it on the line.

play	run	dive	climb	throw
plays	runs	dives	climbs	throws

1 Mia _____ ball with her friends.

2 The children like to _____ together.

3 Juan _____ faster than I do.

4 We _____ on a track team.

She hops.

5 Tom and Kara _____ into the pool.

6 Mary _____ without her goggles.

7 They _____ very tall trees.

8 Liz _____ steep mountains.

9 Juan and Mia _____ balls.

10 I _____ the ball to Juan.

They hop..

More About Subject/Verb Agreement

Fill in the bubble next to the verb that correctly completes the sentence.

1 Bobby _____ a sandwich for lunch.

⬭ bring   ⬭ brings

2 Maria _____ rice and black beans.

⬭ like   ⬭ likes

3 Bobby and Maria _____ lunches.

⬭ trade   ⬭ trades

4 The twins _____ fish sandwiches.

⬭ eat   ⬭ eats

5 The children _____ milk with their lunches.

⬭ drink   ⬭ drinks

6 They _____ fresh fruit for dessert.

⬭ buy   ⬭ buys

7 Jill _____ for a ripe, yellow banana.

⬭ ask   ⬭ asks

8 Aki _____ strawberries and blueberries.

⬭ want   ⬭ wants

9 Nathan _____ grapes on his tray.

⬭ put   ⬭ puts

10 Paulo and Sylvia _____ seats at the table.

⬭ find   ⬭ finds

Verbs have, has, had

 *The verb **have** is irregular. Use **have** or **has** to tell about the present. Use **had** to tell about the past.*

Read each sentence. Write have, has, or had on the line in the sentence. Then write now or past on the line at the end to show if the sentence takes place now or in the past.

1 The man _____ many people in his restaurant last week.

_____

2 He _____ good food in his kitchen.

_____

3 Now the restaurant _____ ten tables.

_____

4 The boy _____ time to help his father today.

_____

5 The girl _____ time, too.

_____

6 The children _____ fun making salads and setting the tables today.

_____

7 They _____ a good time together in the restaurant.

_____

8 They _____ fun yesterday, too.

_____

Verbs have, has, had

The verb **have** *is irregular. Use* **have** *or* **has** *to tell about the present. Use* **had** *to tell about the past.*

Choose the correct word from the chart to complete each sentence.

In the Present	In the Past
have, has	had

1 Joe _____ new running shoes.

2 I _____ new shoes, too.

3 Last week we _____ old shoes.

4 I _____ a green shirt on.

5 Joe _____ a blue shirt on.

6 Yesterday we both _____ red shirts on.

7 Last year we _____ to walk to the park.

8 Now, I _____ skates.

9 Now, Joe _____ a bike.

Verbs have, has, had

Read each sentence. If the underlined word is correct, fill in the last bubble. If not, fill in the bubble next to the correct word.

1 I <u>have</u> a pet bird.

⚪ has   ⚪ had   ⚪ correct as is

2 Now, she <u>had</u> big white wings.

⚪ has   ⚪ have   ⚪ correct as is

3 Before, she <u>has</u> little white wings.

⚪ have   ⚪ had   ⚪ correct as is

4 The baby bird <u>have</u> closed eyes when it was born.

⚪ has   ⚪ had   ⚪ correct as is

5 Now the baby bird <u>had</u> open eyes.

⚪ has   ⚪ have   ⚪ correct as is

6 The mother and baby birds <u>had</u> fun now.

⚪ has   ⚪ have   ⚪ correct as is

7 The baby bird <u>has</u> little wings now.

⚪ have   ⚪ had   ⚪ correct as is

8 It <u>had</u> even smaller wings when it was born.

⚪ has   ⚪ have   ⚪ correct as is

WRITING

Name _____

You're Sharp!

 A sentence begins with a **capital letter.**

Circle the words that show the correct way to begin each sentence.

many Of

Many of

my friends are in Grade 2.

Our teacher

our Teacher

keeps a fish tank in our classroom.

The reading

the reading

centre has many good books.

the globe

The globe

helps us find places around the world.

we Study

We study

about the weather.

Our class

our Class

won the reading contest.

Name _____

Stick With It

 A sentence begins with a **capital letter**.

Write the beginning words correctly to make a sentence.

1. art class _____ begins at noon.

2. today we _____ are making clay pots.

3. first, we _____ form the clay into balls.

4. the next _____ step is to make a hole in the ball.

5. my teacher _____ dries the pots.

6. next week _____ we will paint the pots.

Name _____

A Whale of a Sentence

 A **telling sentence** *ends with a* **period** *(.).*

Rewrite the sentences using capital letters and periods.

1. the blue whale is the largest animal in the world

_____

2. even dinosaurs were not as large as the blue whale

_____

3. blue whales are not part of the fish family

_____

4. the blue whale has no teeth

_____

5. blue whales eat tiny sea creatures

_____

6. blue whales have two blowholes

_____

That Sounds Fishy to Me

 A **telling sentence** *begins with a* **capital letter** *and ends with a* **period.**

Write a sentence about each fish. Remember to tell a complete idea.

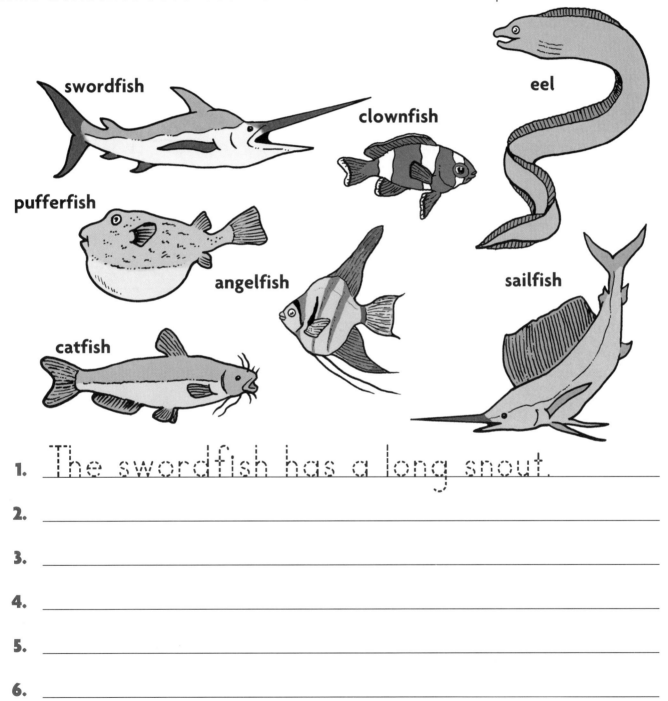

swordfish

pufferfish

catfish

angelfish

clownfish

eel

sailfish

1. The swordfish has a long snout.

2. _____

3. _____

4. _____

5. _____

6. _____

7. _____

Ask Mother Goose

*A sentence that asks a question ends with a **question mark** (?).*
It often begins with one of these words.

Who . . .	*Where . . .*	*Why . . .*	*Could . . .*
What . . .	*When . . .*	*Will . . .*	

Rewrite the questions using capital letters and question marks.

1. where is the king's castle

_____

2. who helped Humpty Dumpty

_____

3. why did the cow jump over the moon

_____

4. will the frog become a prince

_____

5. could the three mice see

_____

Name _____

Name _____

Name _____ *Writing questions*

Ask the Wolf

An **asking sentence** *begins with a* **capital letter** *and ends with a* **question mark** *(?).* It often begins with one of these words.

How . . .   Can . . .   Would . . .
Did . . .   Is . . .   Should . . .

Imagine that you can meet the Big Bad Wolf. What questions would you ask him about Little Red Riding Hood and the Three Little Pigs? Use a different beginning word for each question you write.

1. How _____
2. Did _____
3. Can _____

1. Is _____
2. Should _____
3. Would _____

 Pretend that you are the Big Bad Wolf. Write a sentence on a piece of paper to answer each question above.

Scholastic Success With Writing • Grade 2   215

Is Your Head in the Clouds?

A **telling sentence** *ends with a* **period** *(.).*
An **asking sentence** *ends with a* **question mark** *(?).*

Finish each sentence by putting a period or a question mark in
the cloud at the end.

1. Clouds can look like cotton balls, feathers, or blankets

2. Do you know what makes a cloud form in the sky

3. Have you ever seen dark clouds on rainy days

4. Dark clouds may bring thunderstorms

5. Can you imagine pictures in the clouds

6. White clouds drift across the blue sky

7. Why don't we see clouds every day

8. Rain, snow, sleet and hail may fall from clouds

 Find two telling sentences and two questions in one of your favourite books. Write them on another piece of paper.

Name _____

Sunny Sentences

 *Every sentence begins with a **capital letter**.*
*A **telling sentence** ends with a **period** (.).*
*An **asking sentence** ends with a **question mark** (?).*

Rewrite each sentence correctly.

1. the Sun is the closest star to Earth

_____

2. the Sun is not the brightest star

_____

3. what is the temperature of the Sun

_____

4. the Sun is a ball of hot gas

_____

5. how large is the Sun

_____

6. will the Sun ever burn out

_____

 On a piece of paper, write a sentence with two mistakes. Ask a friend to circle the mistakes.

Camp Fiddlestick

 A telling sentence is called a **statement**. *An asking sentence is called a* **question**.
Now ask yourself:

How do sentences begin? How do statements end? How do questions end?

Write three statements and three questions about the picture.

Statements:

1. _____

2. _____

3. _____

Questions:

1. _____

2. _____

3. _____

 **Sing "Where is Thumbkin?" to yourself. Count the number of questions and statements in
the song.**

A Happy Camper

Complete:

Every sentence begins with a _____.

A statement ends with a _____.

A question ends with a _____.

Uh oh! Dalton was in a hurry when he wrote this letter. Help him find 10 mistakes. Circle them.

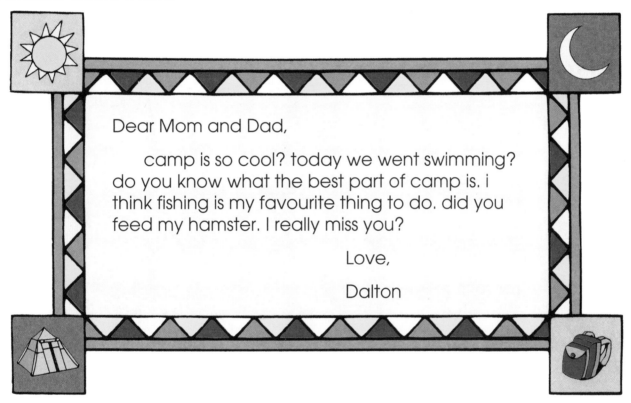

Dear Mom and Dad,

camp is so cool? today we went swimming? do you know what the best part of camp is. i think fishing is my favourite thing to do. did you feed my hamster. I really miss you?

Love,

Dalton

Now choose two questions and two statements from Dalton's letter. Rewrite each correctly.

1. _____

2. _____

3. _____

4. _____

On a piece of paper, write a letter to a friend or family member. Include two statements and two questions.

Name _____

A Day at the Beach

 A sentence that shows strong feeling or excitement is called an **exclamation**. *It ends with an* **exclamation point** *(!). For example: Look at that shark!*

Finish each sentence by putting a period, a question mark, or an exclamation point in the shell at the end.

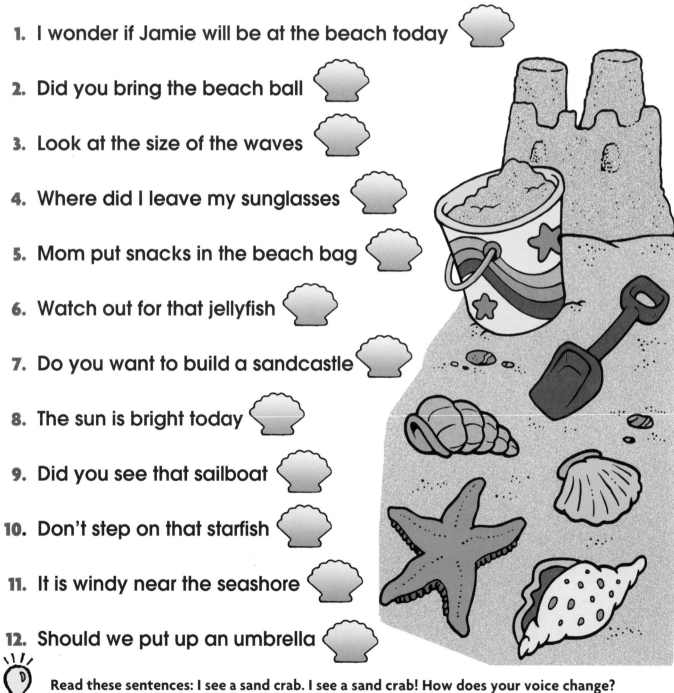

1. I wonder if Jamie will be at the beach today

2. Did you bring the beach ball

3. Look at the size of the waves

4. Where did I leave my sunglasses

5. Mom put snacks in the beach bag

6. Watch out for that jellyfish

7. Do you want to build a sandcastle

8. The sun is bright today

9. Did you see that sailboat

10. Don't step on that starfish

11. It is windy near the seashore

12. Should we put up an umbrella

Read these sentences: I see a sand crab. I see a sand crab! How does your voice change?

Seashore Sentences

Complete:

A _____ *ends with a period.*

A _____ *ends with a question mark.*

An _____ *ends with an exclamation point.*

Write a statement (S), a question (Q), and an exclamation (E) about each picture.

S _____

_____

Q _____

_____

E _____

_____

S _____

_____

Q _____

_____

E _____

_____

On a piece of paper, write a statement, a question and an exclamation about a cartoon in the newspaper.

Building Blocks

 A good sentence has a part that tells who or what the sentence is about. This is called the **subject**.

Make a list of possible subjects to complete each sentence.

_____ jumped the fence.

1. _____

2. _____

3. _____

_____ is too full.

1. _____

2. _____

3. _____

 A good sentence has a part that tells what happens. This is called the **action**.

Make a list of possible actions to complete each sentence.

We _____ on the playground.

1. _____

2. _____

3. _____

The cowboy _____ on his horse.

1. _____

2. _____

3. _____

 On another piece of paper, make a list of five subjects you would like to write about.

Keep Building!

 Some sentences have a part that tells where or when the action is happening.

For each sentence, make a list of possible endings that tell where or when the action happens.

The wind blew _____.

1. _____

2. _____

3. _____

The baby tripped _____.

1. _____

2. _____

3. _____

Complete each sentence.

1. _____ made us laugh last night.

2. The door leads _____.

3. The crowd _____ at the circus.

4. The paint bucket spilled _____.

5. _____ was never seen again.

6. The firefighter _____ into the fire truck.

Get Your Ticket!

Write a sentence to match each picture. Be sure to include a subject, an action, and a part that tells where or when.

A boy climbs a tree in his backyard.

2. _____

3. _____

 Find a cartoon in the newspaper. Use the pictures to write a sentence on another piece of paper. Be sure to include a subject, an action, and a part that tells where or when.

Slide Show

 A sentence is more interesting when it includes a subject, an action, and a part that tells where or when.

Write three sentences and draw pictures to match.

subject	action	where or when

1. _____

subject	action	where or when

2. _____

subject	action	where or when

3. _____

 Switch the sentence parts around to make three silly sentences! Write the sentences on another piece of paper.

Mystery Bags

 Describing words *help you imagine how something looks, feels, smells, sounds, or tastes.*

Make a list of words that describe the object in each bag below.

 Use a paper sack to make a real mystery bag. Place an object in the bag and give describing clues to someone at home. Can he or she guess the mystery object?

Country Roads

 A good sentence uses describing words to help the reader "paint a picture" in his or her mind.

Add a describing word from the list to finish each sentence.

1. The _____ chicken laid

   _____ eggs in her nest.

2. The _____ barn

   keeps the _____

   animals warm at night.

3. _____ carrots grow in

   the _____ garden.

4. Two _____ pigs sleep in

   the _____ pen.

5. The _____ cows drink

   from the _____ pond.

6. A _____ scarecrow

   frightens the _____ birds.

wooden
sunny
lazy
black
three
orange
thirsty
cold
shallow
muddy
funny
fat

 On a piece of paper, write three sentences describing your favourite place to visit.

It's in the Bag

 Describing words *make a sentence more interesting.*

Add a describing word to each sentence.

1. My friend's _____ dog has fleas!

2. The _____ popcorn is in the big bowl.

3. How did the _____ worm get on the sidewalk?

4. The _____ ocean waves crashed against the rocks.

5. The _____ ball broke a window at school!

6. My _____ skin itched from poison ivy.

7. The two _____ squirrels chased each other up the tree.

8. The _____sand felt good on my feet.

9. Are the _____ apples ready to be picked?

10. The _____ ball was hard to catch.

11. Is the _____ salamander hiding under the rock?

12. The _____ snow cone melted quickly.

 Ask someone at home to make a mystery bag and give you clues about the object inside.

City Streets

 A good sentence uses describing words.

Write a statement (S), a question (Q), and an exclamation (E) about the picture. Use each of the following describing words:

fast   busy   crowded

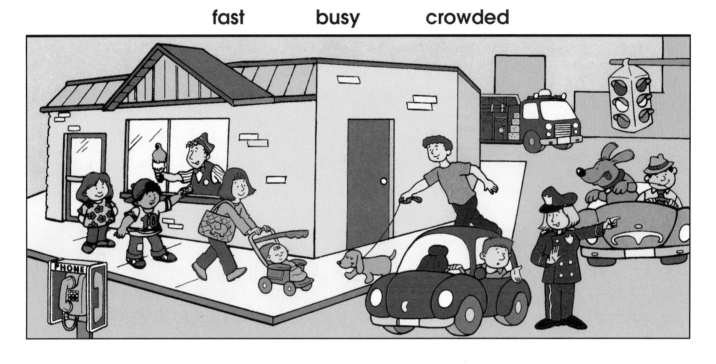

S _____

_____

Q _____

_____

E _____

_____

 Describe a "mystery object" to a friend. Can he or she guess what you are describing?

Football Frenzy

A sentence is more interesting when it gives exact information.

Replace each word to make the sentence more exact.

1. The **ball** game starts **soon**.

   The ___football___ game starts ___now___.

2. We are meeting **her** **there**.

   We are meeting _____ _____.

3. Let's eat **this** and **that** before the game.

   Let's eat _____ and _____ before

   the game.

4. I hope **they** score **some** points.

   I hope _____ score _____ points.

5. **They** were also **there**.

   _____ were also _____.

6. **He** played a **good** game!

   _____ played a _____ game!

Name _____

Take Me Out to the Ball Game

A sentence is more interesting when it gives complete information.

Finish each sentence so that it answers the question.

1. The players get to the stadium when.

_____

2. The team is excited because why.

_____

3. The fans arrive in what.

_____

4. Flags are flying where.

_____

5. A man sings the national anthem when.

_____

6. The fans cheer for whom.

_____

7. The ball is hit where.

_____

 On another piece of paper, write a sentence about your favourite game. Be sure to tell who plays the game with you.

Cake and Ice Cream

 *Two sentences that share the same subject can be combined to make one sentence by using the word **and**.*

Rewrite the sentences by combining their endings.

1. The party was fun.
   The party was exciting.

The party was fun and exciting.

2. We blew up orange balloons.
   We blew up red balloons.

_____

3. We ate cake.
   We ate ice cream.

_____

4. The cake frosting was green.
   The cake frosting was yellow.

_____

5. We made a bookmark.
   We made a clay pot.

_____

6. We brought games.
   We brought prizes.

_____

Name _____

Salt and Pepper

 Two sentences that share the same ending can also be combined to make one sentence.

Rewrite the sentences by combining their subjects.

1. These peanuts are salty!
These pretzels are salty!

These peanuts and pretzels are salty!

2. The first graders eat lunch at noon.
The second graders eat lunch at noon.

_____

3. Where is the salt?
Where is the pepper?

_____

4. The napkins are on the table.
The forks are on the table.

_____

5. Are the muffins in the oven?
Are the cookies in the oven?

_____

6. Mike bought lunch today.
Ava bought lunch today.

_____

Great Gardening Tips

 Sentences can also be combined to make them more interesting. Key words can help put two sentences together.

I will plan my garden. I am waiting for spring.

I will plan my garden while I am waiting for spring.

Combine the two sentences using the key word. Write a new sentence.

1. Fill a cup with water. Add some flower seeds.

_____

2. This will soften the seeds. They are hard.

_____

3. Fill a cup with dirt. The seeds soak in water.

_____

4. Bury the seeds in the cup. The dirt covers them.

_____

5. Add water to the plant. Do not add too much.

_____

6. Set the cup in the sun. The plant will grow.

_____

Name _____

Growing Sentences

 Sentences can be combined to make them more interesting.

Write a combined sentence of your own. Use the given key word to help you.

1. while _I watch TV while my mom makes lunch._

2. until _____

3. because _____

4. but _____

5. or _____

6. and _____

 On another piece of paper, write a combined sentence of your own using one of these key words: *after, before, during.*

The Sky's the Limit

 Some sentences include a list. A **comma** *(,) is used to separate each item in the list.*

For example: Mrs. Jones asked the class to work on pages two, three, and four.

Fill in the blanks to make a list in each sentence. Watch for commas!

1. I ate _____, _____,

and _____ for breakfast.

2. We stayed with Grandma on _____,

_____, and _____ nights.

3. I found _____, _____,

and _____ in my party bag.

4. The boys played _____,

_____, and _____

at summer camp.

5. The _____, _____,

and _____ ate the corn we scattered.

6. The pigs built their houses using _____,

_____, and _____.

 Cut a balloon out of paper. On one side, list three objects that fly. On the other side, write a sentence that lists these objects.

Up, Up, and Away

*Some sentences include a list. A **comma** (,) is used to separate each item in the list.*

Write a sentence that includes a list of the words that are given.

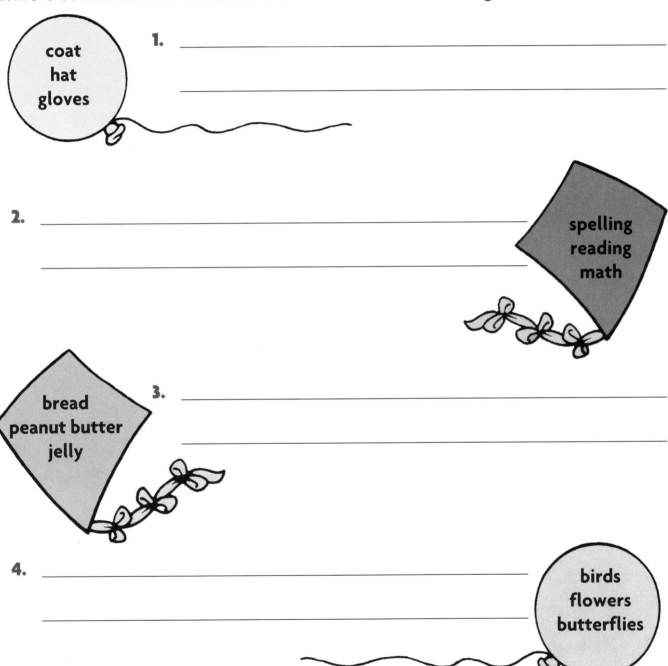

coat
hat
gloves

1. _____

2. _____

spelling
reading
math

bread
peanut butter
jelly

3. _____

4. _____

birds
flowers
butterflies

On a piece of paper, write a sentence that lists colours or shapes of balloons.

Out of This World

*After you write a sentence, go back and look for mistakes. This is called **proofreading** your work.*

Use the proofreading marks to correct the two mistakes in each sentence.

<u>mars</u> = Make a capital letter.　　(?) = Add a question mark.　　(!) = Add an exclamation point.

(.) = Add a period.　　(,) = Add a comma.　　☐ = Add a word. (Write a describing word in the box.)

1. Sometimes I can see mars Jupiter, and Saturn with my telescope.

2. There are ∧stars in our galaxy

3. comets are ∧pieces of ice and rock.

4. The sun is really a ∧star

5. is there life on any other planet

6. Look at that ∧shooting star

7. can you imagine traveling in space

8. i think I saw a ∧alien.

 On a piece of paper, write two sentences about space with two mistakes in each. Ask someone at home to proofread your sentences. Is he or she correct?

Smart About Saturn

 Be sure to proofread your work.

Matthew's science report has nine mistakes. Use proofreading marks to correct his work. Then rewrite the report. Add at least two describing words to the report.

Saturn
by Matthew

Saturn is famous for the rings that surround it? its rings are made of ice, rock and dirt. The rings circle around the planet! Saturn is made of gas? saturn's gases are lighter than water That means Saturn would float if you put it into a tub of water Saturn has at least 53 moons

_____

_____

_____

_____

 On a piece of paper, write a short report about your favourite planet. Be sure to proofread it when you are done.

Name _____

Banana-Rama

Color the word that is missing from each sentence.

1. We _____ a spelling test yesterday. ⌐taked⌐ ⌐took⌐

2. There _____ frost on the ground. ⌐was⌐ ⌐were⌐

3. Tommy _____ the CN Tower. ⌐seen⌐ ⌐saw⌐

4. How _____ elephants are at the zoo? ⌐much⌐ ⌐many⌐

5. Claire _____ her lizard to school. ⌐brought⌐ ⌐brang⌐

6. Have you _____ my dog? ⌐seen⌐ ⌐saw⌐

7. Alyssa _____ a new pair of skates. ⌐gots⌐ ⌐has⌐

8. You _____ supposed to finish your work. ⌐are⌐ ⌐is⌐

9. We _____ standing near a snake! ⌐were⌐ ⌐was⌐

10. They _____ a pig in the mud. ⌐seen⌐ ⌐saw⌐

11. We _____ our winter boots. ⌐wore⌐ ⌐weared⌐

12. Is she _____ to come over? ⌐gonna⌐ ⌐going⌐

13. _____ your cat climb trees? ⌐Do⌐ ⌐Does⌐

14. Rosie _____ cookies to the bake sale. ⌐brang⌐ ⌐brought⌐

An Apple a Day

Find the word that is incorrect in each sentence. Draw an apple around it and write the correct word on the line.

1. Laura brang a snack to camp. _____

2. I seen the sea lion show at the zoo. _____

3. Gabe gots a dinosaur collection. _____

4. Erin taked her dog for a walk. _____

5. We is going to see the movie. _____

6. Jason runned to the playground. _____

7. How many pennies do you got? _____

8. The kids was having fun. _____

9. Did you saw the soccer game? _____

10. How much do that cost? _____

11. Naya brang her cat to school! _____

12. I does my homework after school. _____

Stories of Nature

 Sentences should be written in the correct order to tell a story.

Finish the stories by writing a sentence about each of the last two pictures.

First: Two birds build a nest.

Next: _____

Last: _____

First: A flower bud grows.

Next: _____

Last: _____

Name _____

Nestled in a Nest

Write a sentence about each picture to make your own story.

 Read your story to a friend.

Stories on Parade

*Stories have a **beginning** (B), a **middle** (M), and an **end** (E).*

Write a middle sentence that tells what happens next. Then write an ending sentence that tells what happens last.

B During the parade, five funny clowns jumped out of a purple bus.

M Next, _____

E Last, _____

B A big balloon got loose in the wind.

M Next, _____

E Last, _____

B A group of horses stopped right in front of us.

M Next, _____

E Last, _____

B Some clowns were riding motorcycles.

M Next, _____

E Last, _____

On a piece of paper, draw a picture of a parade that shows what is happening in the stories you wrote.

An Original Story

Choose a story idea from the list. Then write a beginning, middle, and ending sentence to make a story of your own. Colour a picture to match each part.

The Best Birthday Ever   **King for a Day**

My Dog's Dream   **The Magic Rock**

B

First: _____

_____

_____

_____

M

Next: _____

_____

_____

_____

E

Last: _____

_____

_____

_____

Staple three pieces of paper together to make a book. Write another story and draw a picture for each part.

Once Upon a Time

 The setting of a story tells when or where it is happening.

Imagine that you are writing a story for each picture below. How will you describe the setting? Write a sentence describing each setting.

setting	→	characters	→	problem	→	solution

It was a hot morning in the desert.

 On a piece of paper, describe the setting of your favourite movie.

Name _____

All Kinds of Characters

 The people or animals in a story are called **characters**.

Some characters are likable and others are not. Write a describing sentence about each character. Be sure to give each character a name.

| setting | → | characters | → | problem | → | solution |

On a piece of paper, make a list of four people you know well. Write three words that describe each of them. Cross out the four names and write animal names instead.

That's a Problem!

*To make a story exciting, one of the characters often runs into a **problem**.*

Think about each character in the sentences below. What could happen that would make a problem for that character? Write the next sentence creating a problem.

| setting | → | characters | → | problem | → | solution |

1. Beauty Butterfly was enjoying the warm spring day.

_____

2. Jesse was supposed to wear shoes outside.

_____

3. Gabby could not wait to bite into her apple.

_____

4. Ben smacked the baseball into the air.

_____

5. Barney Bass had never seen such a big worm!

_____

Good Solution!

At the end of a story, the problem is usually solved. This is called the solution.

Read the beginning and middle parts of the stories below. Write an ending solution for each.

| setting | → | characters | → | problem | → | solution |

Noah and his dog, Spot, were best friends. They went everywhere together. At bedtime, Noah whistled for Spot to jump in his bed. One winter night, Noah whistled and whistled, but Spot did not come.

_____

_____

_____

Josh loved Grade 2, but he did not like recess. Josh's class was always the last one out to the playground. Every day, Josh ran to get a swing, but they were always taken.

_____

_____

On a piece of paper, make a list of three problems you have faced. How did you solve each problem?

The Mighty Knight

 *A **story map** helps you plan the setting, characters, problem, and solution.*

Write a sentence about each part of the map to make a story.

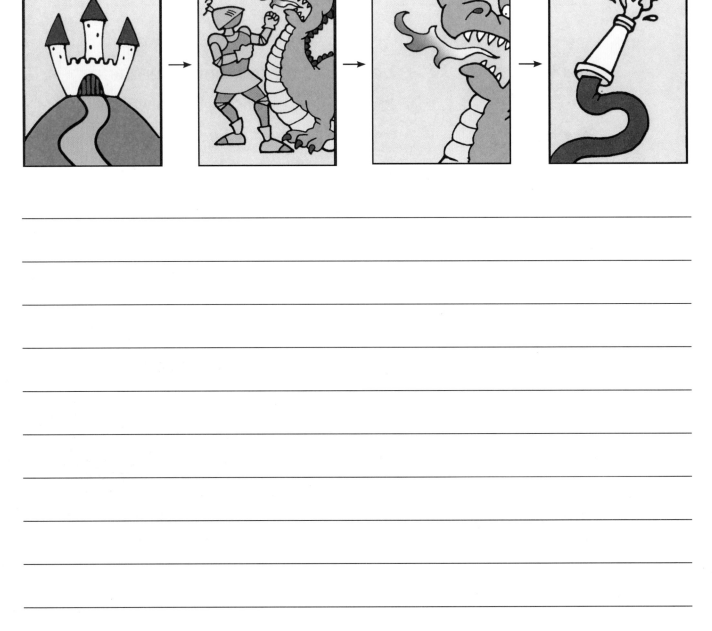

_____

_____

_____

_____

_____

_____

_____

_____

 Read your story to a friend.

A Story Fit for a King

Use a story map to help plan your story before you begin writing.

Complete the map. Then use it to write a story "fit for a king."

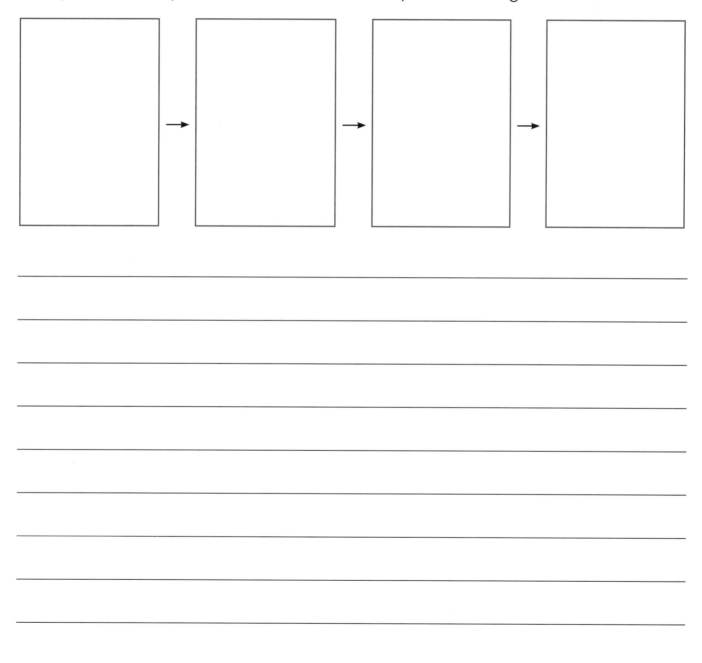

_____

_____

_____

_____

_____

_____

_____

_____

Turn your story into a puppet show! Perform your puppet show for someone at home.

Scholastic Success With

MAPS

Looking at a Map

Have you ever been in an airplane? Did you look down on Earth? Then you know that things look different from above.

This photo was taken from an airplane. It shows a community below.

Circle **YES** if you see the thing in the photo.
Circle **NO** if you do not.

1.	building	YES	NO
2.	street	YES	NO
3.	car	YES	NO
4.	train	YES	NO

5. **What else do you see?** _____

The map on this page shows the same place as the photo. A **map** is a drawing of a place from above. A map shows where things are.

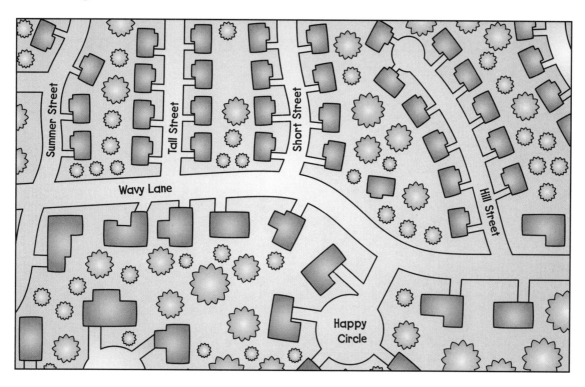

1. Find the house on the corner of Summer Street and Wavy Lane on the map. Make an X on that house.

2. Find a swimming pool in the photo.
   Draw it in the same place on the map.

3. How are the map and photo alike? _____

   _____

4. How are the map and photo different? _____

   _____

A Globe and Earth

Pretend you are in a spaceship. You look out and see a planet. It is Earth, your home. This photo shows what Earth looks like from space. It looks like a big blue marble. Isn't it beautiful?

1. You can see only one side of Earth at a time.

   What shape is Earth? _____

2. Does Earth have more land or water? _____

3. Why is part of Earth green? _____

Have you ever played with a toy car? A toy car is a model of a real car. This picture shows a globe. A **globe** is a model of Earth. You can see that the globe and Earth are the same shape.

1. What shape is a globe? _____

2. Is the globe bigger or smaller than Earth? _____

3. What do the words on the globe tell you? _____

_____

A World Map

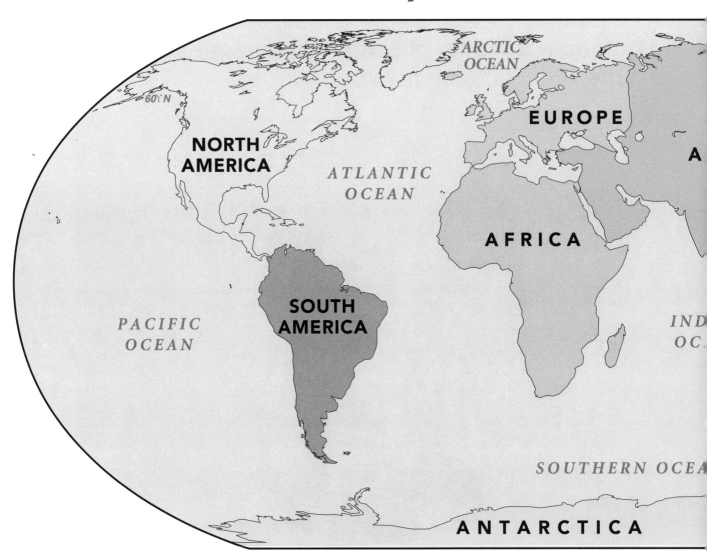

A globe is handy for finding places on Earth.
A world map can show all of Earth, too.

1. This map shows Earth's continents. A continent is a large body
    of land. Can you find all seven of Earth's continents? Write an
    X on each one.

Name _____   **World**

PACIFIC
OCEAN

RALIA/OCEANIA

2. The map also shows Earth's oceans.

An ocean is a large body of salt water.

How many oceans do you see?

_____

3. Name four continents that begin with "A."

_____

_____

_____

_____

4. Name two oceans that begin with "A."

_____

_____

5. How is a world map different from a globe?

_____

_____

A Compass Rose

This is a **compass rose**. A compass rose is a symbol that helps you read a map. The arrows on a compass rose point to the four main **directions**. They are north, south, east, and west.

North is the direction toward the North Pole.

South is the direction toward the South Pole.

When you face north, west is on the left. East is on the right.

Sometimes a compass rose has letters that stand for the direction words.

1. **N stands for** _____

2. **S stands for** _____

3. **E stands for** _____

4. **W stands for** _____

Name _____

Map of the World

1. What continent is south of
   South America and Africa? _____

2. What ocean is north of
   North America and Europe? _____

3. Draw a straight line from the North Pole to the South Pole.
   Are these places east or west of your line?

   Indian Ocean _____   North America _____

   Europe _____   Australia _____

Using Directions

When you use a map, look for the compass rose.
Use the directions to tell you how to get places.

Pretend you are at this park. Use a pencil to trace the way you go.

1. Start at the gate and go east. What do you see? _____

2. Go to the swings. In which direction are they? _____

3. Next you come to a fountain.
   In which direction did you walk? _____

4. If you go north, what will you see? _____

Lucy lives in Fun City. Her house is on Chuckles Street.
Find Lucy's house.

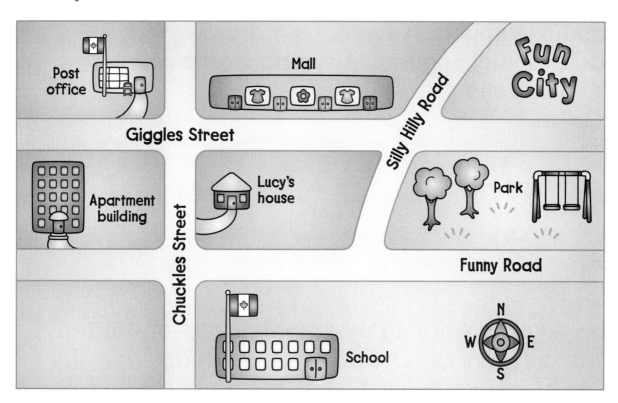

Circle the correct answers.

1. **To get to the park, Lucy goes _____.**
   west   east   south

2. **The mall is _____ of Lucy's house.**
   north   south   west

3. **The post office is _____ of the mall.**
   south   east   west

4. **When Lucy walks to school, she heads _____.**
   north   west   south

5. **If Lucy walks west on Funny Road, she will be at the _____.**
   park   library   apartment building

Map Symbols

A map has **symbols**. A symbol is a drawing that stands for something real. A symbol can also be a colour or a pattern.

Woods   **Water**   **Wetlands**

A map key tells what each symbol stands for. Study the map key. Find each symbol on the map. Write the number of the symbol in the correct circle on the map.

Map Reading

Use the map key and the compass rose to answer the questions.

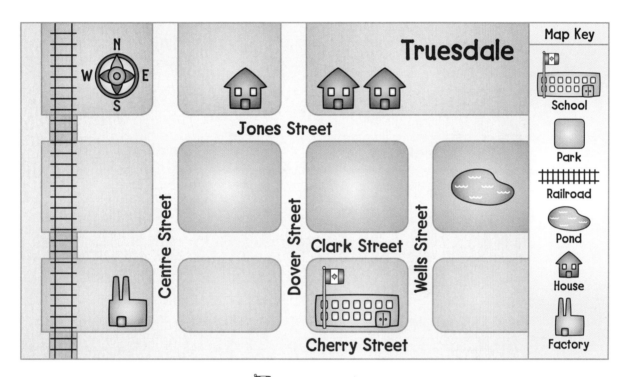

1. What does the symbol mean? _____

2. What street is north of the school? _____

3. What is just west of the factory? _____

4. What colour is used to show the park? _____

5. Is the park north or south of the houses? _____

Using Map Symbols

Welcome to the zoo! You can use this map to get around.

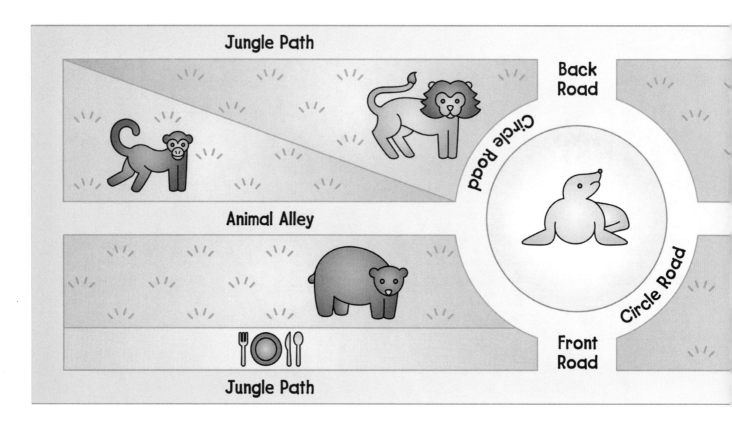

Most zoos have maps for visitors to use.
Use the map to answer the questions.

1. What does this symbol mean? _____

2. Are the elephants on the
   east or west side of the zoo? _____

3. Can you get a snack at this zoo? _____

4. Are the monkeys north or south of the bears? _____

5. On what road are the seals? _____

6. Does this zoo have lions? _____

7. Does this zoo have hippos? _____

8. The map key is missing a snake symbol.
   Draw a snake symbol in the map key.

9. Find the space south of the elephants.
   Add your snake symbol there.

Distance

A map can show how far it is from one place to another. This is called **distance**.

Look at these lines.

A.

B.

C.

Circle YES or **NO**.

1. Line A is the longest line.   YES   NO

2. Line C is the shortest line.   YES   NO

3. Line B is longer than Line C.   YES   NO

4. Line C is longer than Line A.   YES   NO

5. Line B is shorter than Line A.   YES   NO

6. Line C is longer than Line B.   YES   NO

Name _____

The Tang family is playing catch.
This map shows where each player is standing.

Use a ruler to help answer the questions.

1. The longest distance is between Ellen and _____ .

2. The shortest distance is between Jason and _____ .

3. Is Buddy farther from Mom or Ellen? _____ .

4. Is Dad nearer to Mom or Buddy? _____ .

5. It is almost the same distance between
   Ellen and Mom and Mom and _____ .

A Map Grid

Some maps have lines like this:
These lines form a **grid**.
A grid is a pattern
of lines that
form squares.

Each square on
a grid has a letter
and a number.
Find the letter "A"
at the side of the
map. Then find the
number 1 at the
top of the map.
The first square
in the top row is A1.
Can you find A2?

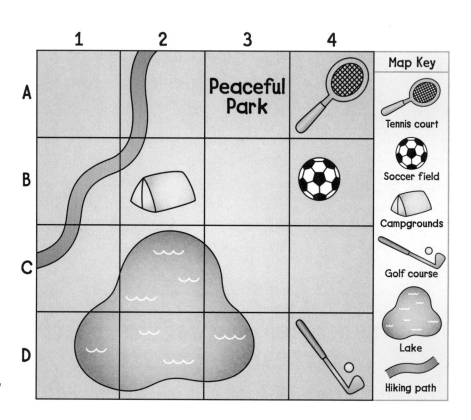

Use the grid to answer the questions.

1. What is in A4? _____

2. In what square is the soccer field? _____

3. Find D4. What can you do there? _____

4. Through what squares does the hiking path go? _____

Here is a map grid game you can play. Study the map. Then look for each square below. Write the square "name" (letter and number) under each picture.

_____

_____

_____

_____

_____

_____

Name _____

Using a Map Grid

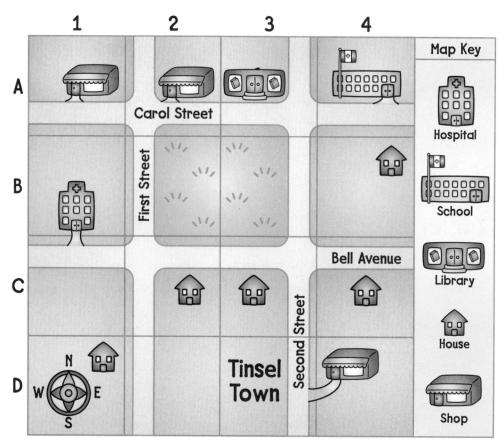

A grid helps you find places on a map. Use the grid to answer the questions.

1. In which square is the hospital? _____

2. What is in square C4? _____

3. What street runs through squares A2, B2, C2, and D2? _____

4. Can you shop in D1? _____

5. You want to borrow a book. In which square would you look? _____

Landforms

These pictures show different parts of Earth called **landforms**.

A landform is a shape of land such as a mountain. You can see that Earth has many different landforms.

A **plain** is flat land.

1. How is a mountain different from a plain?

   _____

2. Through what kind of landform does a river often flow?

   _____

A **valley** is low land between

hills or mountains.

3. What are two ways you could get to an island?

   _____

4. Which type of land is best for farming?

   Why? _____

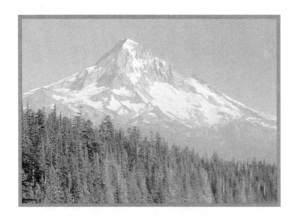

A **mountain** is very high land.

A **hill** is land that is higher than a plain, but not as high as a mountain.

An **island** is land with water all around it.

5. Which landform is good for skiing? _____

   Why? _____

6. Which landforms can you see near your house?

   _____

   _____

Bodies of Water

Earth has different bodies of water, too.

You found five oceans on page 258-259.
They are the largest bodies of water on Earth.

An **ocean** is a large body of salt water.

A **river** is a long body of water that flows across the land.

A **lake** is water with land all around it.

Use the pictures to answer the questions.

1. Which body of water would take the longest time to cross? _____

2. What are some things you might do on a lake? _____

3. How are rivers and lakes different? _____

_____

The picture shows different kinds of land and water.

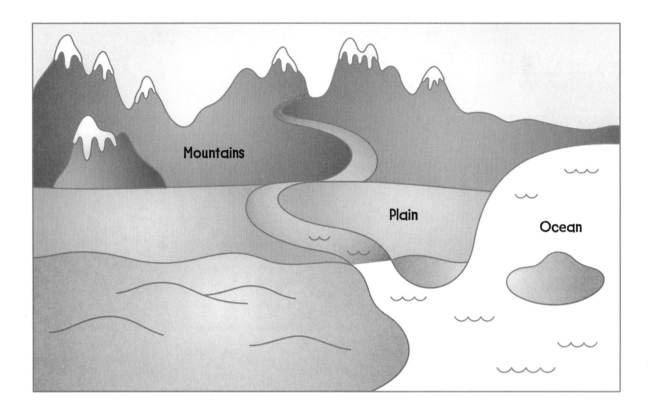

1. Find the low land between the mountains.
   Write valley on it.

2. Find the ocean. Colour it blue.

3. Find land that has water all around it.
   Write the name on this land.

4. Find land that is higher than the plain, but not as high as the mountains. Add the correct label to this land.

North America

Can you name Earth's seven continents?

One of them is North America. You live in North America.
Canada is one country on this continent.
A country is a land and the people who live there.
Mexico and the United States are two other countries in
North America. Find them on the map on page 278.

Use the map to answer these questions.

1. What does the symbol —————
   stand for? _____

2. What is the country south of Canada? _____

3. In which direction is Mexico from the United States? _____

4. What is the capital of Canada? _____

5. Is the Pacific Ocean to the east or
   west of North America? _____

6. What U.S. state is separated from the
   United States by Canada? _____

7. What river forms the border between
   the United States and Mexico? _____

8. Which country is larger, Canada or Mexico? _____

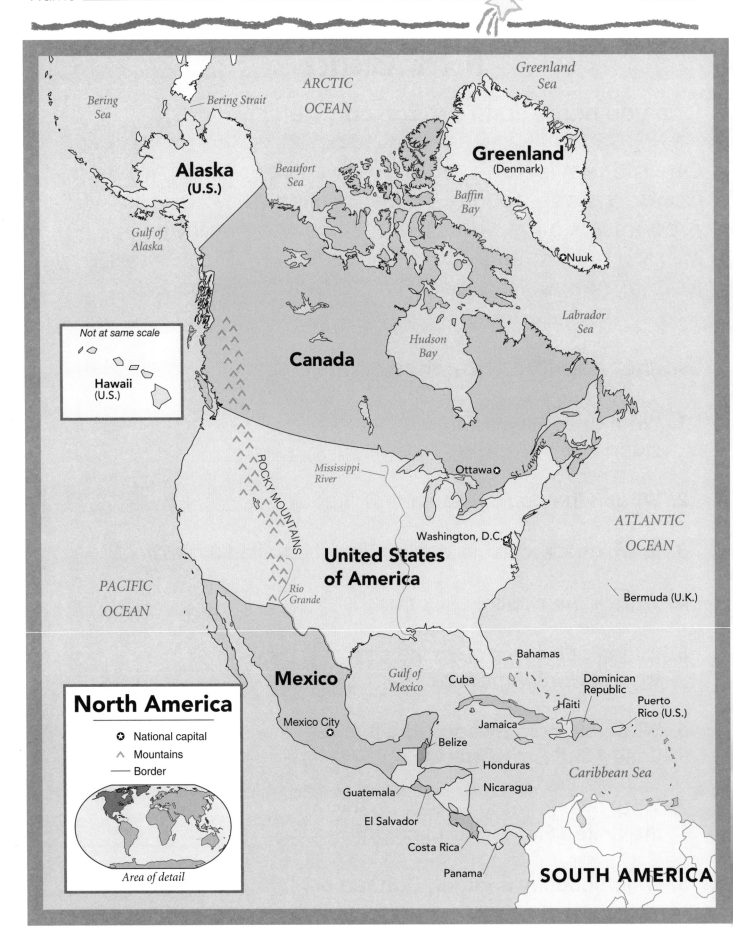

ARCTIC OCEAN

Bering Sea

Bering Strait

Greenland Sea

Alaska (U.S.)

Beaufort Sea

Greenland (Denmark)

Baffin Bay

Gulf of Alaska

Not at same scale

Hawaii (U.S.)

Nuuk

Labrador Sea

Hudson Bay

Canada

ROCKY MOUNTAINS

Mississippi River

Ottawa ✪

St. Lawrence

United States of America

ATLANTIC OCEAN

Washington, D.C. ✪

PACIFIC OCEAN

Rio Grande

Bermuda (U.K.)

North America

✪ National capital
∧ Mountains
— Border

Area of detail

Mexico

Gulf of Mexico

Bahamas

Cuba

Dominican Republic

Haiti

Puerto Rico (U.S.)

Mexico City ✪

Jamaica

Belize

Honduras

Caribbean Sea

Guatemala

Nicaragua

El Salvador

Costa Rica

Panama

SOUTH AMERICA

Map Review

Use the map to answer the questions.

1. What does the symbol mean?

   _____

2. What is the symbol for library?

   _____

3. What does the letter "S" mean on the compass rose? _____

4. What is in square C1? _____

5. In which direction is the hospital from the park? _____

6. Is the school east or west of the library? _____

7. Amy lives on First Street. In what square is her house? _____

8. Amy takes the bus to school. Name the streets that the bus route follows.

   _____

Thinking About Maps

You have learned a lot about maps. Use what you know to find the secret words.

1. This symbol helps you find directions.

   _ _ _ _ _ _ _
     1   4

2. Where do you look to see what symbols mean?

   _ _ _ _ _
     3

3. Land with water all around it.

   _ _ _ _ _
       2

4. Plains and hills are types of

   _ _ _ _ _ _ _
     5   8   6

5. North America is a

   _ _ _ _ _ _ _
     10   7

6. This landform is very high land.

   _ _ _ _ _ _
     9

Now, can you figure out the secret message?

   _ _ _ _ _ _ _ _ _ _
   1 2 3 4 5 6 7 8 9 10

Glossary

border
A border shows where places begin and end.

capital
A capital is a city where government leaders work. Ottawa is the capital of Canada.

compass rose
A compass rose is a symbol that helps you read a map. A compass rose shows the four main directions.

continent
A continent is a large body of land. Earth has seven continents.

country
A country is a land and the people who live there. Canada is a country.

direction
A direction tells where something is. The four main directions are north, south, east, and west.

distance
Distance is how far it is from one place to another.

globe
A globe is a model of Earth.

grid
A grid is a pattern of lines that form squares.

hill
A hill is land that is higher than a plain but not as high as a mountain.

island
An island is land with water all around it.

Glossary

lake
A lake is a body of water with land all around it.

landform
A landform is a shape of land such as a mountain. map

A map is a drawing of a place from above. A map shows where things are.

map key
A map key is a list of symbols on a map. A map key tells what each symbol means.

mountain
A mountain is very high land.

ocean
An ocean is a large body of salt water. Earth has five oceans.

plain
A plain is flat land.

river
A river is a long body of water that flows across the land.

route
A route is a way to go from one place to another.

symbol
A symbol is a drawing that stands for something real. A symbol can also be a colour or a pattern.

valley
A valley is low land between hills or mountains.

ADDITION & SUBTRACTION

Spell It Out

Add. Complete the puzzle using number words.

Across

1. 5 + 5 = _____

2. 3 + _____ = 7

3. 2 + _____ = 9

6. 6 + 2 = _____

7. _____ + 0 = 1

Down

1. 4 + _____ = 6

2. 2 + _____ = 7

3. _____ + 4 = 10

4. 4 + 5 = _____

5. 5 + _____ = 8

 Finish each number sentence with a number word.

five + two = _____   three + six = _____

Name _____

Beautiful Bouquets

Subtract. Draw petals to show the difference.

💡 **Colour the bows with an even number yellow.**
Colour the bows with an odd number purple.

Name _____

Crazy Creatures

Add or subtract. Fill in each missing number.

Name _____

Can You See It?

Write the numbers you see with a . . .

A.
sum of **5** and
difference of **1**.

B.
sum of **17** and
difference of **7**.

C.
sum of **14** and
difference of **2**.

D.
sum of **18** and
difference of **4**.

E.
sum of **12** and
difference of **2**.

F.
sum of **15** and
difference of **9**.

G.
sum of **5** and
difference of **3**.

H.
sum of **18** and
difference of **2**.

I.
sum of **13** and
difference of **5**.

J.
sum of **16** and
difference of **6**.

 Make your own number glasses.
sum of _____ and
difference of _____

Name _____

**Adding 1-digit and 2-digit
numbers without regrouping**

Scarecrow Sam

Why doesn't Scarecrow Sam tell secrets when he is near Farmer Joe's

bean patch? _____

To find out the answer, add the numbers. Circle the pumpkins that have
sums of 14, and write the letters that appear inside those pumpkins in order
in the boxes below.

288   Scholastic Success With Addition & Subtraction • Grade 2

You've Got Mail!

1. Solve the problems.

2. Find each number pair on the graph. Make a dot for each.

3. Connect the dots in the order that you make them.

4. What picture did you make?

_____

	Across	Up
1.	$20 + 7 =$ _____	$12 + 12 =$ _____
2.	$12 + 3 =$ _____	$11 + 13 =$ _____
3.	$1 + 2 =$ _____	$10 + 14 =$ _____
4.	$13 + 2 =$ _____	$10 + 5 =$ _____
5.	$13 + 14 =$ _____	$21 + 3 =$ _____
6.	$23 + 4 =$ _____	$11 + 4 =$ _____
7.	$5 + 22 =$ _____	$2 + 4 =$ _____
8.	$3 + 12 =$ _____	$1 + 5 =$ _____
9.	$3 + 0 =$ _____	$6 + 0 =$ _____
10.	$2 + 1 =$ _____	$2 + 13 =$ _____
11.	$0 + 3 =$ _____	$2 + 22 =$ _____

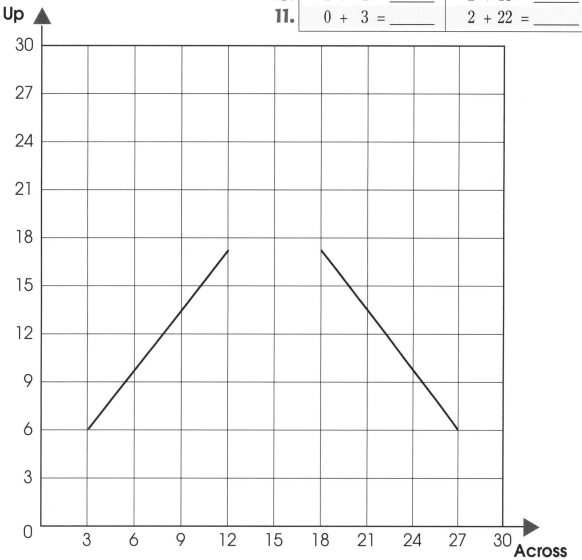

Name _____

Counting on Good Manners

Add. Then use the code to write a letter in each oval to find the "good manner" words.

May I have some candy, please?

11 + 10	62 + 31	44 + 34	41 + 5	13 + 31	35 + 43

◯ ◯ ◯ ◯ ◯ ◯

40 + 10	43 + 24	42 + 4	54 + 25	41 + 42

◯ ◯ ◯ ◯ ◯

57 + 2	22 + 3	34 + 32

◯ ◯ ◯

54 + 5	21 + 4	41 + 25	21 + 11	26 + 52

◯ ◯ ◯ , ◯ ◯

Thank you!

50 + 30	70 + 8	50 + 43	11 + 7	15 + 10	31 + 4	17 + 61

◯ ◯ ◯ ◯ ◯ ◯ ◯

Code

18 C	21 P	25 O	32 R	35 M	44 S	46 A	50 T
59 Y	66 U	67 H	78 E	79 N	80 W	83 K	93 L

Name _____

Just the Same

Add. Connect the flowers with the same sum.

43
+ 26

18
+ 70

11
+ 34

62
+ 35

13
+ 12

52
+ 36

23
+ 22

51
+ 18

14
+ 11

55
+ 42

Make matching sums.

___ + ___   ___ + ___   ___ + ___   ___ + ___
   78   78   54   54

Planet Earth

Add.

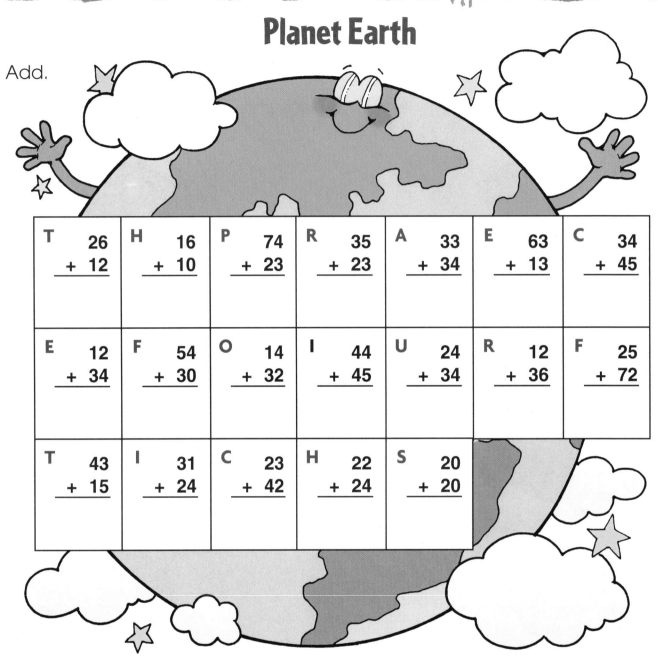

T 26 + 12	**H** 16 + 10	**P** 74 + 23	**R** 35 + 23	**A** 33 + 34	**E** 63 + 13	**C** 34 + 45
E 12 + 34	**F** 54 + 30	**O** 14 + 32	**I** 44 + 45	**U** 24 + 34	**R** 12 + 36	**F** 25 + 72
T 43 + 15	**I** 31 + 24	**C** 23 + 42	**H** 22 + 24	**S** 20 + 20		

For each sum that is an even number, write its letter below in order.

How much of the earth is covered by water?

___ ___ ___ ___ ___ — ___ ___ ___ ___ ___ ___ ___

For each sum that is an odd number, write its letter below in order.

What is the biggest ocean?

___ ___ ___ ___ ___ ___ ___

Name _____

Glorious and Free

Add. Use the code to find the secret words.

12 + 11	63 + 12	68 + 31	55 + 20	34 + 13	24 + 10	41 + 34	53 + 46

◯ ◯ ◯ ◯ ◯ ◯ ◯ ◯

40 + 45	26 + 72	23 + 10	35 + 43	20 + 43	53 + 34	22 + 10	11 + 34	64 + 14	65 + 33

32 + 33	25 + 21	25 + 30	44 + 54	76 + 12	21 + 11	11 + 10

40 + 11	62 + 24	32 + 43	52 + 12

◯ ◯ ◯ ◯

Code

23 C	34 I	47 D	51 F	64 G	75 A	86 L	99 N

Name _____

Subtracting 1-digit numbers

Detective Work

Use the code to help Detective Dave discover the secret phone number. The first problem has been done for you.

1	2	3
4	5	6
7	8	9

1.

$7 - 1 = 6$

2.

$\square - \square = \underline{\ }$

3.

$\square - \square = \underline{\ }$

4.

$\square - \square = \underline{\ }$

5.

$\square - \square = \underline{\ }$

6.

$\square - \square = \underline{\ }$

7.

$\square - \square = \underline{\ }$

The phone number is:

$\underline{\ }\ \underline{\ }\ \underline{\ }\ -\ \underline{\ }\ \underline{\ }\ \underline{\ }\ \underline{\ }$

294 Scholastic Success With Addition & Subtraction • Grade 2

Name _____

Chirp, Chirp!

1. Solve the problems.

2. Find each number pair on the graph. Make a dot for each.

3. Connect the dots in the order that you make them.

4. What picture did you make?

_____

	Across	Up
1.	10 – 7 = _____	10 – 8 = _____
2.	4 – 2 = _____	3 – 1 = _____
3.	7 – 5 = _____	1 – 0 = _____
4.	8 – 0 = _____	1 – 0 = _____
5.	9 – 1 = _____	8 – 6 = _____
6.	10 – 3 = _____	7 – 5 = _____
7.	10 – 2 = _____	8 – 2 = _____
8.	8 – 3 = _____	10 – 0 = _____
9.	9 – 7 = _____	7 – 1 = _____
10.	4 – 1 = _____	5 – 3 = _____
11.	9 – 2 = _____	6 – 4 = _____

Winter Is Coming

Do the subtraction problems. Help Mr. Squirrel find his way
to the tree where he is storing acorns for the winter. Make
sure he doesn't cross any odd answers.

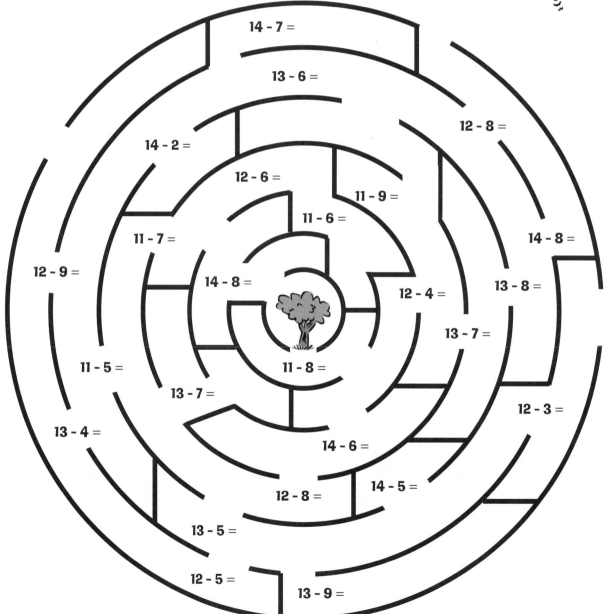

14 - 7 =

13 - 6 =

12 - 8 =

14 - 2 =

12 - 6 =

11 - 9 =

11 - 6 =

11 - 7 =

14 - 8 =

12 - 9 =

14 - 8 =

12 - 4 =

13 - 8 =

13 - 7 =

11 - 5 =

11 - 8 =

13 - 7 =

12 - 3 =

13 - 4 =

14 - 6 =

14 - 5 =

12 - 8 =

13 - 5 =

12 - 5 =

13 - 9 =

Name _____

Baseball Puzzle

What animal can always be found at a baseball game?

_____

To find out, do the subtraction problems. If the answer is greater than 9,
colour the shapes black. If the answer is less than 10, colour the shapes red.

Bubble Yum!

1. Solve the problems.

2. Find each number pair on the graph. Make a dot for each.

3. Connect the dots in the order that you make them.

4. What picture did you make?

	Across	Up
1.	27 – 23 = _____	58 – 53 = _____
2.	18 – 15 = _____	23 – 21 = _____
3.	30 – 27 = _____	29 – 28 = _____
4.	18 – 11 = _____	46 – 45 = _____
5.	58 – 51 = _____	17 – 15 = _____
6.	28 – 22 = _____	49 – 44 = _____
7.	19 – 15 = _____	77 – 72 = _____

_____

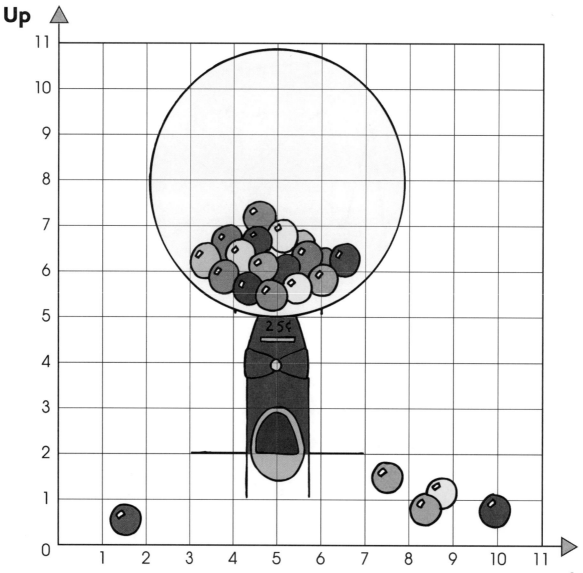

Super Star

Solve the problems. If the answer is between 1 and 20, colour the shape red.
If the answer is between 21 and 40, colour the shape white. If the answer is
between 41 and 90, colour the shape blue.

Taking It Further: Write five subtraction problems that have answers between
10 and 20.

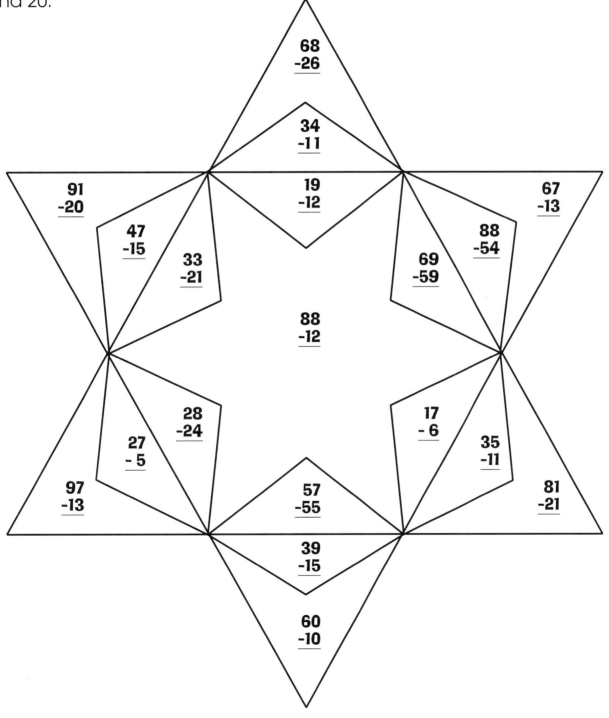

Name _____

Moving West

Subtract. Follow the even sums to guide the settlers to their new home.

58 − 33

74 − 60

99 − 27

35 − 11

57 − 33

95 − 43

86 − 42

65 − 22

94 − 41

63 − 41

48 − 22

47 − 25

68 − 44

53 − 41

66 − 24

74 − 32

34 − 13

97 − 42

61 − 21

86 − 53

74 − 63

54 − 10

49 − 15

82 − 62

76 − 26

83 − 61

79 − 25

37 − 13

76 − 55

29 − 16

24 − 14

69 − 41

98 − 24

57 − 23

45 − 13

88 − 46

High Flying

Subtract.

$$96 - 34$$

$$59 - 26$$

$$65 - 42$$

$$81 - 51$$

$$43 - 22$$

$$78 - 64$$

$$84 - 23$$

$$37 - 15$$

$$92 - 51$$

Colour the bird with the smallest number in the ones place red.

Colour the bird with the smallest number in the tens place blue.

Colour each bird with the same number in the ones and tens place green.

Weather Drops

Subtract. Using the difference in each rain drop, write the weather words in order of their differences from least to greatest by the umbrella handle. Then colour your favourite kind of "weather drop" blue.

blizzard
59
− 18
41

lightning
63
− 10

storm
81
− 11

hail
80
− 30

snow
77
− 12

blizzard

fog
88
− 46

thunder
96
− 25

rain
87
− 25

frost
75
− 31

wind
97
− 23

Name _____

Animal Families

Subtract.

$$\begin{array}{r} 96 \\ -\ 42 \\ \hline \end{array}$$

$$\begin{array}{r} 97 \\ -\ 12 \\ \hline \end{array}$$

$$\begin{array}{r} 86 \\ -\ 43 \\ \hline \end{array}$$

$$\begin{array}{r} 99 \\ -\ 14 \\ \hline \end{array}$$

$$\begin{array}{r} 98 \\ -\ 55 \\ \hline \end{array}$$

$$\begin{array}{r} 78 \\ -\ 24 \\ \hline \end{array}$$

$$\begin{array}{r} 89 \\ -\ 22 \\ \hline \end{array}$$

$$\begin{array}{r} 77 \\ -\ 34 \\ \hline \end{array}$$

$$\begin{array}{r} 78 \\ -\ 11 \\ \hline \end{array}$$

$$\begin{array}{r} 95 \\ -\ 63 \\ \hline \end{array}$$

$$\begin{array}{r} 88 \\ -\ 56 \\ \hline \end{array}$$

 Colour the animals using the colour code.

red	blue	purple	yellow	green
32	43	54	67	85

Triple the Fun

Add. Write the sum on each bowl.

 Colour bowls with 1, 5, or 8 in the ones place yellow.
Colour bowls with 0, 4, or 7 in the ones place pink.
Colour bowls with 2, 6, or 9 in the ones place brown.

A Great Catch

Circle each group of 10. Write the number of tens and ones on the chart.
Then write the number on the baseball glove.

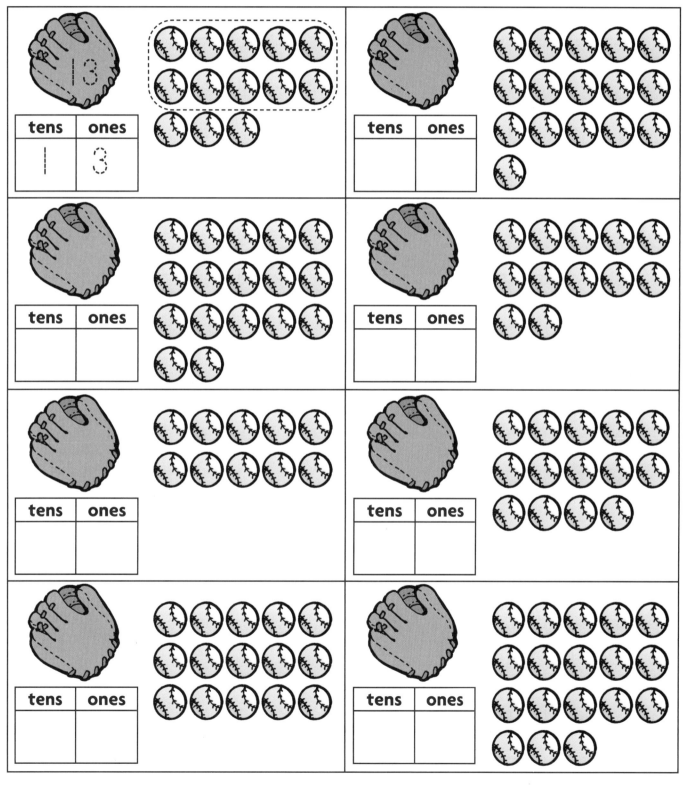

tens	ones
1	3

Kaleidoscope

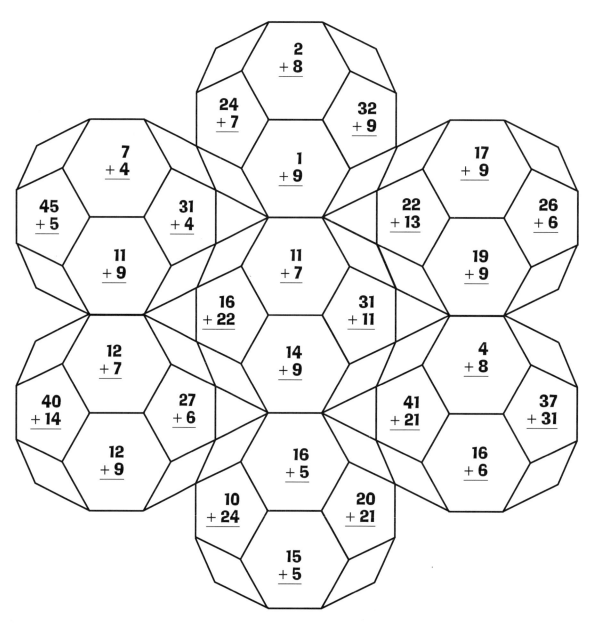

Solve the problems.

If the answer is between 1 and 30, colour the shape red.

If the answer is between 31 and 99, colour the shape grey.

Finish by colouring the other shapes with the colours of your choice.

Extra: Name two numbers that when added together equal 27.

_____ + _____ = _____   _____ + _____ = _____

Zoo Animal

1. Solve the problems.

2. Find each number pair on the graph. Make a dot for each.

3. Connect the dots in the order that you make them.

4. What picture did you make?

_____

	Across	Up
1.	13 + 7 = ____	12 + 4 = ____
2.	15 + 9 = ____	5 + 3 = ____
3.	11 + 9 = ____	0 + 4 = ____
4.	19 + 9 = ____	2 + 2 = ____
5.	10 + 18 = ____	11 + 5 = ____
6.	16 + 16 = ____	9 + 7 = ____
7.	28 + 8 = ____	2 + 6 = ____

	Across	Up
8.	17 + 15 = ____	1 + 3 = ____
9.	31 + 9 = ____	3 + 1 = ____
10.	8 + 32 = ____	8 + 8 = ____
11.	19 + 25 = ____	19 + 1 = ____
12.	27 + 17 = ____	18 + 14 = ____
13.	7 + 29 = ____	17 + 23 = ____
14.	18 + 6 = ____	25 + 15 = ____

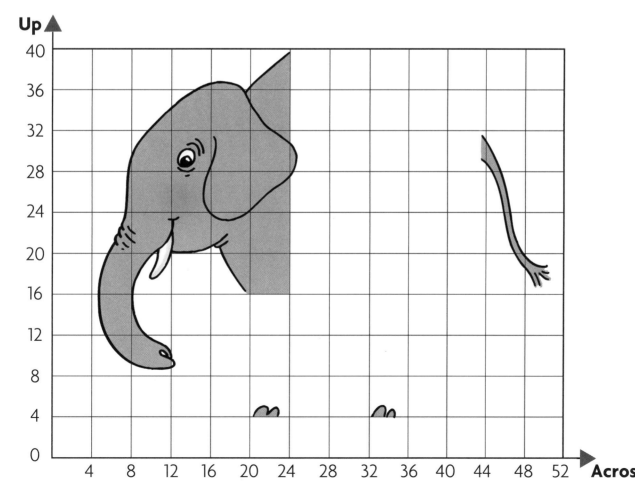

Name _____

Don't Forget Your Keys

Add. Then follow the clue to find the right key. Write the sum in the key hole.

A.
43
+ 9

87
+ 6

64
+ 8

Find the key with the greatest number in the tens place.

B.
36
+ 5

55
+ 7

29
+ 8

Find the key with the greatest number in the ones place.

C.
14
+ 9

43
+ 7

58
+ 4

Find the key with even numbers in the ones and tens places.

D.
53
+ 7

24
+ 8

75
+ 6

Find the key with 0 in the ones place.

E.
84
+ 6

36
+ 8

67
+ 9

Find the key with the same number in the ones and tens places.

Name _____

Treasure of a Book

Add. Then colour each box with an odd sum to help the boy find his way to the book. Hint: Remember to look in the ones place.

47 + 24	74 + 19	78 + 12	15 + 37

48 + 44	31 + 59	52 + 39	29 + 57	73 + 19
63 + 18	14 + 67	57 + 16	24 + 18	63 + 29
57 + 28	27 + 47	76 + 16	72 + 18	76 + 18
32 + 19	17 + 24	55 + 38	32 + 49	

How Do We Get There?

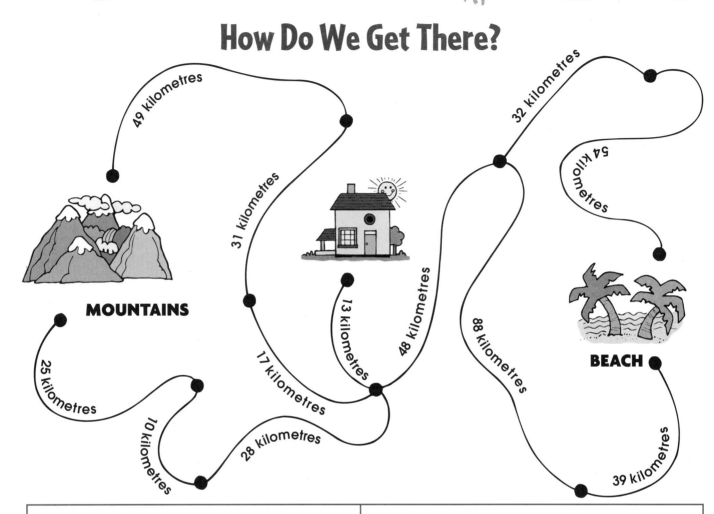

49 kilometres

32 kilometres

54 kilometres

31 kilometres

MOUNTAINS

13 kilometres

48 kilometres

88 kilometres

BEACH

25 kilometres

17 kilometres

10 kilometres

28 kilometres

39 kilometres

Add the distance of each route from the house to the beach.		Add the distance of each route from the house to the mountains.	
Route #1	Route #2	Route #1	Route #2
_____	_____	_____	_____
_____	_____	_____	_____
_____	_____	_____	_____
_____	_____	_____	_____
+ _____	+ _____	+ _____	+ _____
km	km	km	km

Name _____

Crossdigit Wiz

Find the sums of the three addends in the rows across and down.
The answer circles are numbered.

You can do it!

| 8 | 6 | 7 | ◯ 1. |

| 13 | 8 | 5 | ◯ 2. | | 5 |
| 7 | 4 | 3 | ◯ 3. | | 10 |

| 8 | 16 | 7 | ◯ 4. | 20 |

| 9 | | ◯ 5. |

| 30 | 10 | 4 | 9 | 15 | ◯ |

| 21 | 7. ◯ | 6 | | | 6. |

| 7 | | 16 | 5 | 8 | ◯ 8. |

◯ 9.

| 11 |

◯ 10.

Name _____

Carnival Fun

Do the problems below. Then find your answers hidden in the carnival scene and circle them. Can you find all twelve answers?

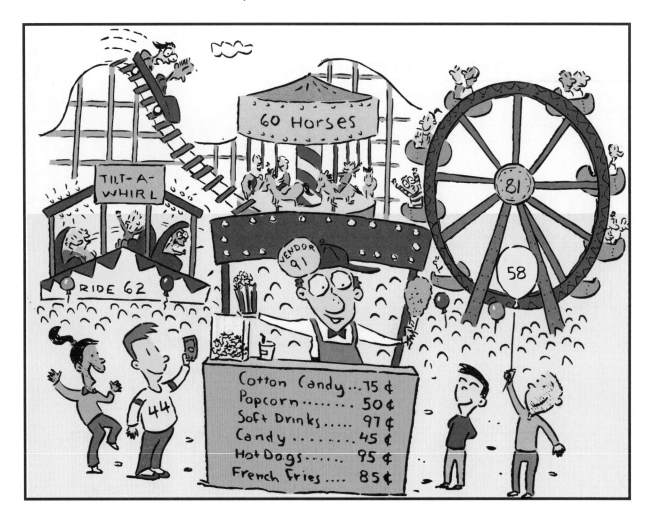

```
   15        27        34        15        16        12
   33        23        23        25        14        31
 + 27      + 12      + 24      + 10      + 14      + 17


   28        43        10        29        37        51
   22        27        17        13        31        23
 + 45      + 27      + 18      + 16      + 17      + 17
```

Crack the Numbers

Look at the number on each chick. Write the number of tens and ones on the egg. Then trade one ten for ten ones.

35   3 tens   5 ones
      2 tens
      15 ones

47   ___ tens   ___ ones
      ___ tens
      ___ ones

82   ___ tens   ___ ones
      ___ tens
      ___ ones

94   ___ tens   ___ ones
      ___ tens
      ___ ones

61   ___ tens   ___ ones
      ___ tens
      ___ ones

90   ___ tens   ___ ones
      ___ tens
      ___ ones

Digging Up Bones

Help Daisy find a delicious bone! Subtract.
Circle the answer that goes with each bone.

> is greater than and < is less than

A.

> 40 and < 70

56	94
− 8	− 5

B.
> 25 and < 55

87	53
− 8	− 7

C.

> 37 and < 82

45	81
− 9	− 5

D.
> 74 and < 96

83	68
− 6	− 9

E.
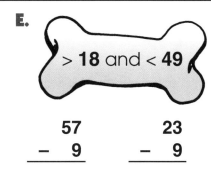
> 18 and < 49

57	23
− 9	− 9

F.
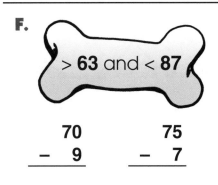
> 63 and < 87

70	75
− 9	− 7

G.
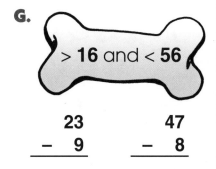
> 16 and < 56

23	47
− 9	− 8

**Write two subtraction
problems on another
piece of paper. One
answer should match
the bone.**

> 48 and < 87

Name _____

First, Next, Last

Subtract. Then number the pictures in order from least to greatest.

A.

64	58	83
− 45	− 19	− 46

B.

83	24	28
− 75	− 18	− 19

C.

53	54	51
− 25	− 17	− 37

D.

88	91	82
− 59	− 53	− 45

E.

73	71	76
− 44	− 35	− 28

F.

82	34	57
− 64	− 19	− 38

Name _____

Purdy Bird

Purdy the Parakeet loves to look at herself in the mirror. Only one of these parakeets below really shows what Purdy looks like in the mirror. Can you find the right one? To check your answer, do the subtraction problems next to each bird. The answer for the correct bird is 24.

$$35 - 17$$ $$62 - 28$$

$$53 - 14$$ $$92 - 27$$ $$82 - 23$$ $$83 - 28$$

$$67 - 48$$ $$58 - 29$$ $$72 - 17$$ $$73 - 58$$

$$42 - 26$$ $$90 - 81$$ $$52 - 28$$ $$56 - 19$$

Grandma's Quilt

Solve the problems. If the answer is between 1 and 50, colour the shape red.
If the answer is between 51 and 100, colour the shape blue. Finish the design
by colouring the other shapes with the colours of your choice.

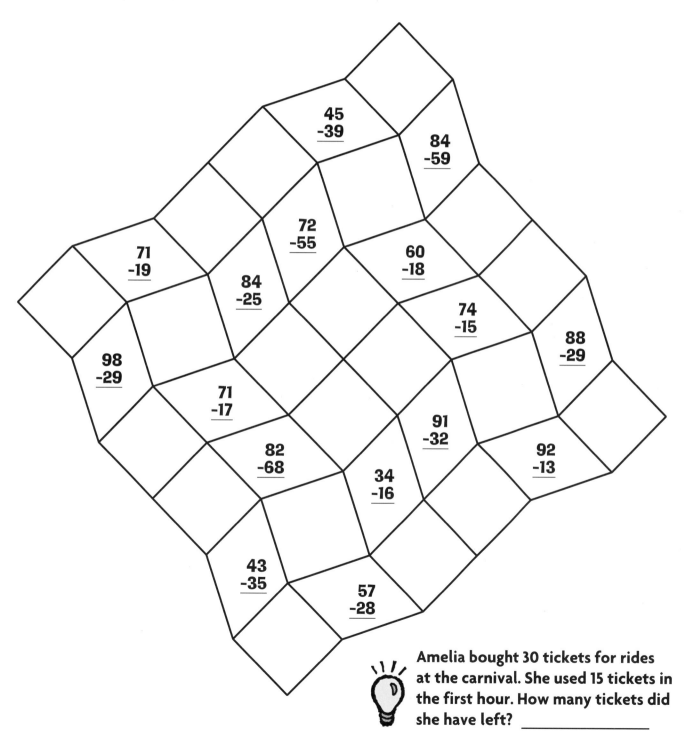

Amelia bought 30 tickets for rides
at the carnival. She used 15 tickets in
the first hour. How many tickets did
she have left? _____

Name _____

All Tied Up

Subtract. Add to check.

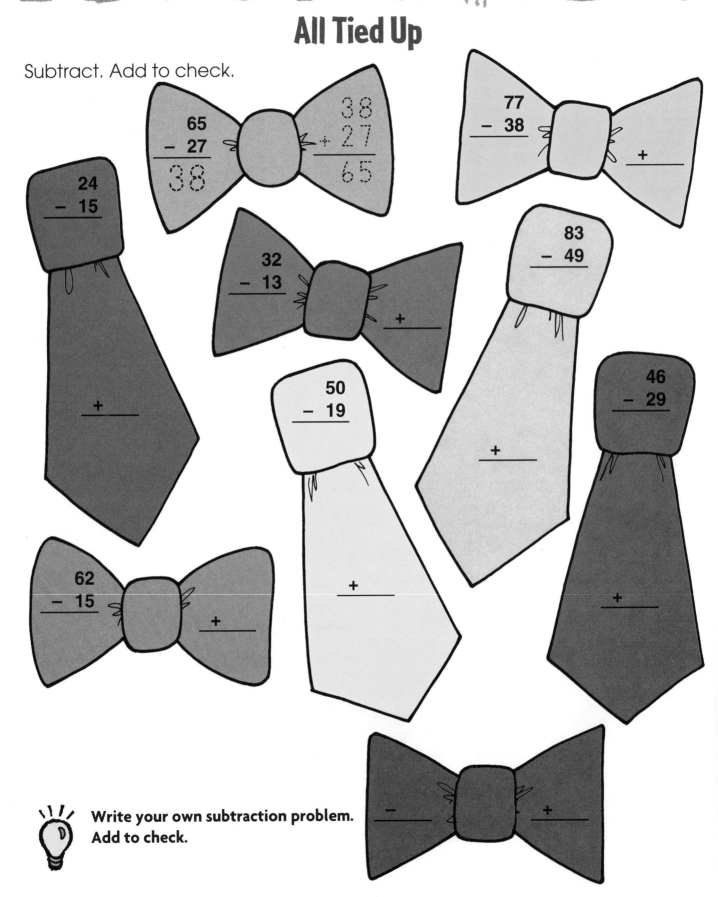

$$\begin{array}{r} 65 \\ -\ 27 \\ \hline 38 \end{array} \qquad \begin{array}{r} 38 \\ +\ 27 \\ \hline 65 \end{array}$$

$$\begin{array}{r} 77 \\ -\ 38 \\ \hline \end{array} \qquad +$$

$$\begin{array}{r} 24 \\ -\ 15 \\ \hline \end{array}$$

$$\begin{array}{r} 32 \\ -\ 13 \\ \hline \end{array} \qquad +$$

$$\begin{array}{r} 83 \\ -\ 49 \\ \hline \end{array}$$

$$+$$

$$\begin{array}{r} 50 \\ -\ 19 \\ \hline \end{array}$$

$$\begin{array}{r} 46 \\ -\ 29 \\ \hline \end{array}$$

$$+$$

$$+$$

$$+$$

$$\begin{array}{r} 62 \\ -\ 15 \\ \hline \end{array} \qquad +$$

Write your own subtraction problem.
Add to check.

$$-\qquad\qquad +$$

Teenie Tiny Babies

Add or subtract.

| U. | 42
+ 39 | L. | 53
− 48 | N. | 31
+ 29 | C. | 74
− 28 | O. | 44
+ 46 |

| P. | 75
− 37 | H. | 40
− 17 | K. | 27
+ 36 | S. | 96
− 48 | A. | 62
− 48 |

| G. | 80
− 62 | M. | 55
+ 16 | R. | 88
− 19 |

Write the letter that goes with each number.

I am smaller than your
thumb when I'm born.

__ __ __ __ __ __ __ __
63　14　60　18　14　69　90　90

I am even smaller.

__ __ __ __ __
63　90　14　5　14

I am smaller than a bumblebee.

__ __ __ __ __ __ __
90　38　90　48　48　81　71

Since we are so little, we
live right next to our mothers in a safe, warm

__ __ __ __ __
38　90　81　46　23

Name _____

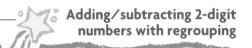

Adding/subtracting 2-digit
numbers with regrouping

Day by Day

Add or subtract. Colour each special date on the calendar.

July

Sun.	Mon.	Tues.	Wed.	Thur.	Fri.	Sat.
		1	2	3	4	5
6	7	8	9	10	11	12
13	14	15	16	17	18	19
20	21	22	23	24	25	26
27	28	29	30	31		

A. Camp begins one week after the second Monday. Colour this date red.

B. The baseball game is two weeks before the fourth Wednesday. Colour this date green.

C. The birthday party is two weeks after the second Saturday. Colour this date purple.

D. The swim meet is three weeks before the fifth Tuesday. Colour this date blue.

E. The trip to the zoo is one week before the third Sunday. Colour this date orange.

F. The picnic is two weeks before the fifth Thursday. Colour this date yellow.

G. What date is 14 days after the third Wednesday? Colour this date pink.

H. What date is 18 days before the fourth Friday? Colour this date brown.

Name _____

Pizza Vote

Use the circle graph to compare the
results of the pizza vote.

(sausage, veggie, cheese, pepperoni, mushroom, onion — 9, 13, 25, 28, 12, 11)

A. How many students voted for
pepperoni and cheese in all?

B. How many more students
voted for cheese than veggie?

C. How many more students
voted for pepperoni than
sausage?

D. How many students voted for
mushroom and veggie
altogether?

E. How many more students
voted for mushroom than
veggie?

F. How many students voted for
sausage and pepperoni in all?

G. How many students voted for
veggie, cheese, and mushroom
in all?

💡 **Find the total number of students who voted.**

Name _____

Tool Time

Find the sum of the numbers in each tool.

$$\begin{array}{r} 34 \\ 27 \\ +\ 5 \\ \hline \end{array}$$

+ ___

+ ___

+ ___

A. Write the number found in the and .

Write the number found in the and .

$$\boxed{}$$
$$\boxed{}$$
$$+ \underline{}$$

Find the sum.

B. Find the difference between the largest and smallest numbers in each tool.

 − ___   − ___   − ___

 On another piece of paper, find the sum of the tools altogether.
Hint: You'll be adding nine numbers.

Hundreds of Pumpkins

Regroup tens into hundreds. Remember: 10 tens = 1 hundred. Write the number of hundreds and the number of remaining tens.

27 tens
2 hundreds
7 tens

84 tens
_____ hundreds
_____ tens

93 tens
_____ hundreds
_____ tens

71 tens
_____ hundreds
_____ tens

56 tens
_____ hundreds
_____ tens

32 tens
_____ hundreds
_____ tens

49 tens
_____ hundreds
_____ tens

65 tens
_____ hundreds
_____ tens

Write the number.

5 hundreds **7 tens** **0 ones**

8 hundreds **0 tens** **4 ones**

Name _____

Name _____

Name _____

Through the Tunnels

Add. Then trace the mole's path to the top. The mole must travel through tunnels with a zero in the sum.

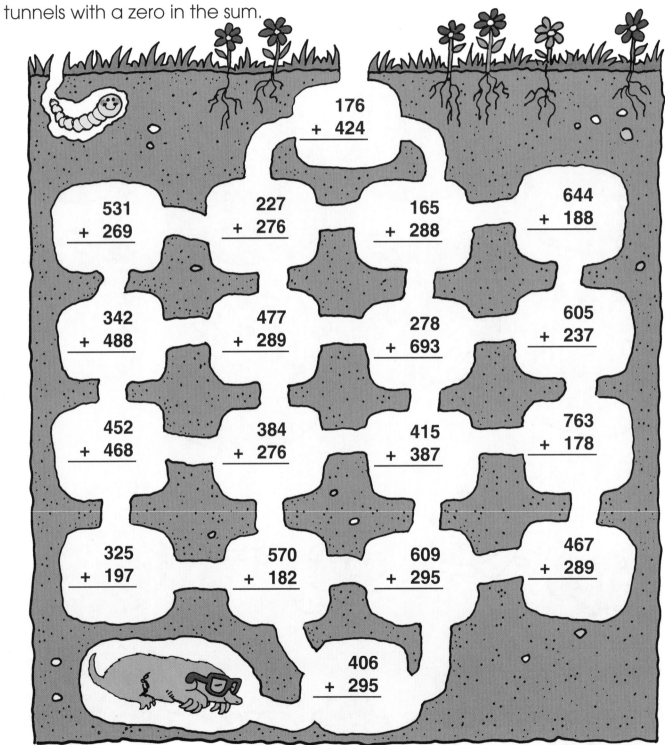

$$\begin{array}{r} 176 \\ + \ 424 \\ \hline \end{array}$$

$$\begin{array}{r} 531 \\ + \ 269 \\ \hline \end{array} \qquad \begin{array}{r} 227 \\ + \ 276 \\ \hline \end{array} \qquad \begin{array}{r} 165 \\ + \ 288 \\ \hline \end{array} \qquad \begin{array}{r} 644 \\ + \ 188 \\ \hline \end{array}$$

$$\begin{array}{r} 342 \\ + \ 488 \\ \hline \end{array} \qquad \begin{array}{r} 477 \\ + \ 289 \\ \hline \end{array} \qquad \begin{array}{r} 278 \\ + \ 693 \\ \hline \end{array} \qquad \begin{array}{r} 605 \\ + \ 237 \\ \hline \end{array}$$

$$\begin{array}{r} 452 \\ + \ 468 \\ \hline \end{array} \qquad \begin{array}{r} 384 \\ + \ 276 \\ \hline \end{array} \qquad \begin{array}{r} 415 \\ + \ 387 \\ \hline \end{array} \qquad \begin{array}{r} 763 \\ + \ 178 \\ \hline \end{array}$$

$$\begin{array}{r} 325 \\ + \ 197 \\ \hline \end{array} \qquad \begin{array}{r} 570 \\ + \ 182 \\ \hline \end{array} \qquad \begin{array}{r} 609 \\ + \ 295 \\ \hline \end{array} \qquad \begin{array}{r} 467 \\ + \ 289 \\ \hline \end{array}$$

$$\begin{array}{r} 406 \\ + \ 295 \\ \hline \end{array}$$

On another piece of paper, write three more problems that have a zero in the sum.

Tricky Twins

Sandy and Mandy are having a twin party. There are six sets of twins, but only one set of identical twins. To find the identical twins, solve the addition problems under each person. The identical twins have the same answer.

```
  207
+ 544
```

```
  126
+  89
```

```
  328
+ 348
```

```
  257
+ 458
```

```
  547
+ 129
```

```
  624
+ 127
```

```
  108
+ 107
```

```
  229
+ 418
```

```
  258
+ 268
```

```
  379
+ 336
```

```
  417
+ 109
```

```
  153
+ 494
```

Eager Leader

Fill in the missing numbers.

```
  2 _ 8            4 0 _
+ _ 5 _          + 3   5
  6 7 9            _ 1 8
```

```
  2 _ 7            3 _ _            1 2 5
+ _ 5 _          + 1 2 4          + _ _ _
  3 9 8            _ 7 8            4 7 9
```

How are you doing?

```
  1 5 _                             5 _ 8
+ 3 _ 2                           + _ 6 _
  _ 9 2                             7 6 9
```

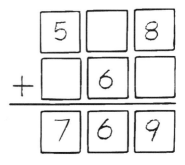

```
  4 _ _            1 4 6            3 1 4
+ 2 2 0          + _ 3 _          + _ _ _
  _ 7 9            3 _ 8            4 3 7
```

Name _____

Sandwich Shop

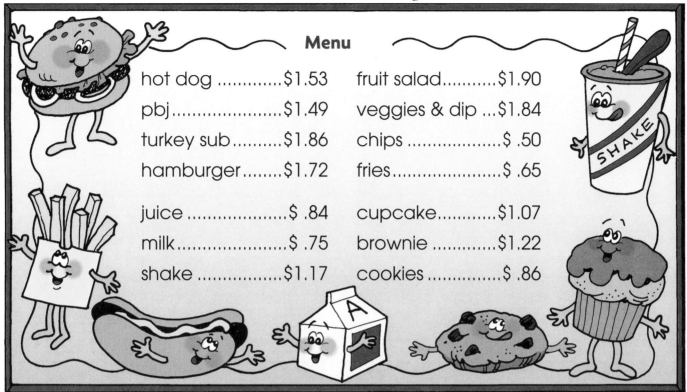

Menu

hot dog	.............$1.53	fruit salad	............$1.90
pbj	....................$1.49	veggies & dip	...$1.84
turkey sub	.........$1.86	chips	..................$ .50
hamburger	........$1.72	fries	....................$ .65
juice	....................$ .84	cupcake	............$1.07
milk	.....................$ .75	brownie	.............$1.22
shake	.................$1.17	cookies	..............$ .86

Add.

A.

pbj
chips
milk
brownie   + _____

B.

hamburger
fries
shake   + _____

C.

turkey sub
veggies & dip
juice   + _____
cupcake

D.

hot dog
fruit salad
brownie
juice   + _____

E.

turkey sub
chips
shake   + _____

F.

pbj
cookies
milk   + _____

Name _____

Easy as 1, 2, 3

Add to find the perimeter of each shape.

A.

B.

C.

Text

$$
\begin{array}{r}
123 \\
406 \\
+\ 406 \\
\hline
\end{array}
$$

$$+ \underline{\qquad}$$

$$+ \underline{\qquad}$$

D.

E.

F.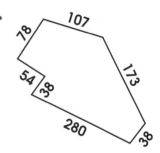

$$+ \underline{\qquad}$$

$$+ \underline{\qquad}$$

$$+ \underline{\qquad}$$

 Colour each shape using the code below.

9 hundreds — orange	4 tens — red	3 ones — purple
6 hundreds — green	7 tens — yellow	8 ones — blue

Count Down

Regroup hundreds to tens. Remember: 1 hundred = 10 tens.

4 hundreds ___ tens

2 hundreds ___ tens

7 hundreds ___ tens

5 hundreds ___ tens

1 hundred ___ tens

9 hundreds ___ tens

8 hundreds ___ tens

3 hundreds ___ tens

Name _____

The Sun's Family

Draw a line to each matching difference to connect each planet to a fact about it.

Mars

694
− 421

Saturn

935
− 123

Mercury

573
− 241

Pluto

937
− 304

Earth

437
− 225

Uranus

968
− 413

397
− 185

I am a ball of rock and metal but covered with soil, rock, and water.

982
− 650

I am a bare, rocky ball similar to Earth's moon.

847
− 214

I am a dwarf planet and not a true planet.

963
− 151

I am surrounded by seven flat rings made of pieces of ice and rock.

857
− 302

I am a planet with 27 moons.

596
− 323

I am called the Red Planet.

Name _____

A Place in Space

Draw a line to each matching difference to connect each planet or space object to a fact about it.

Venus $\begin{array}{r} 713 \\ -\ 171 \\ \hline \end{array}$	$\begin{array}{r} 952 \\ -\ 236 \\ \hline \end{array}$ I am a planet with days lasting only 16 hours.
Neptune $\begin{array}{r} 833 \\ -\ 117 \\ \hline \end{array}$	$\begin{array}{r} 857 \\ -\ 469 \\ \hline \end{array}$ I am like a dirty snowball made of dust, ice, and gases.
Jupiter $\begin{array}{r} 675 \\ -\ 216 \\ \hline \end{array}$	$\begin{array}{r} 612 \\ -\ 428 \\ \hline \end{array}$ I am covered with craters.
Moon $\begin{array}{r} 407 \\ -\ 223 \\ \hline \end{array}$	$\begin{array}{r} 931 \\ -\ 389 \\ \hline \end{array}$ I am sizzling hot with no water.
Comet $\begin{array}{r} 514 \\ -\ 126 \\ \hline \end{array}$	$\begin{array}{r} 892 \\ -\ 433 \\ \hline \end{array}$ I am a giant planet with a red spot.

 Complete each pattern. Then tell someone the pattern for each set of numbers.

900, 800, 700, _____, _____, _____, _____, _____, _____

900, 700, 500, _____, _____

800, 600, 400, _____

Name _____

Tricky Zero

Subtract.

$$\begin{array}{r} 190 \\ -\ 124 \\ \hline \end{array}$$

$$\begin{array}{r} 360 \\ -\ 318 \\ \hline \end{array}$$

$$\begin{array}{r} 720 \\ -\ 517 \\ \hline \end{array}$$

$$\begin{array}{r} 480 \\ -\ 136 \\ \hline \end{array}$$

$$\begin{array}{r} 502 \\ -\ 289 \\ \hline \end{array}$$

$$\begin{array}{r} 208 \\ -\ 129 \\ \hline \end{array}$$

$$\begin{array}{r} 500 \\ -\ 247 \\ \hline \end{array}$$

$$\begin{array}{r} 904 \\ -\ 435 \\ \hline \end{array}$$

$$\begin{array}{r} 490 \\ -\ 256 \\ \hline \end{array}$$

$$\begin{array}{r} 800 \\ -\ 643 \\ \hline \end{array}$$

$$\begin{array}{r} 305 \\ -\ 176 \\ \hline \end{array}$$

$$\begin{array}{r} 300 \\ -\ 134 \\ \hline \end{array}$$

$$\begin{array}{r} 700 \\ -\ 391 \\ \hline \end{array}$$

Treasures Under the Sea

Add or subtract. Use the chart to colour the picture.

53	white
187	pink
264	brown
319	purple
420	green
837	blue
900	yellow

780 − 727

249 + 588

618 − 198

741 − 422

244 − 191

906 − 587

555 + 345

941 − 104

271 + 149

433 − 380

299 + 121

554 − 290

483 − 296

902 − 638

625 − 438

367 + 533

Follow the Trees

Add or subtract. Then trace the bear's path to its cave. The bear follows trees with sums that have a 3 in the tens place.

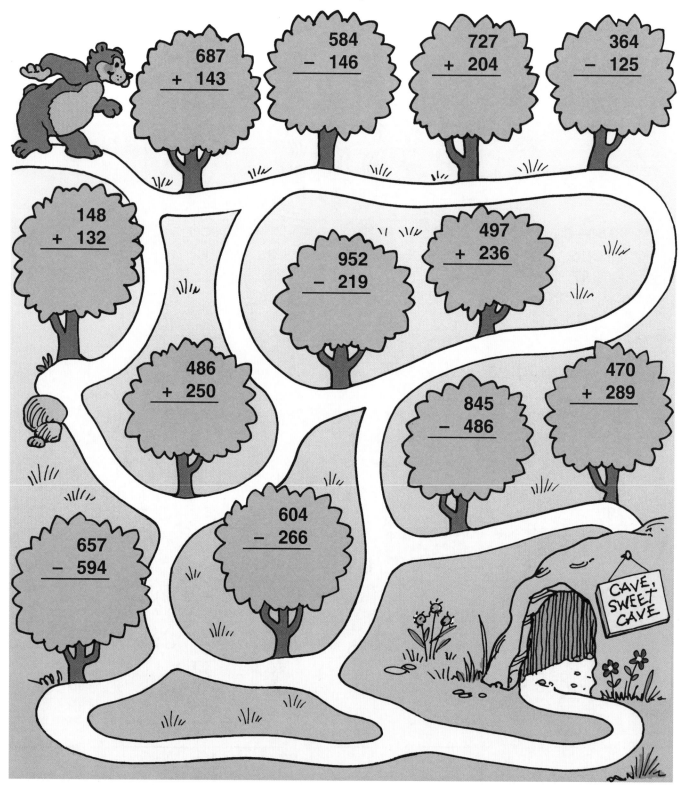

687
+ 143

584
− 146

727
+ 204

364
− 125

148
+ 132

952
− 219

497
+ 236

486
+ 250

845
− 486

470
+ 289

657
− 594

604
− 266

Name _____

School Supplies

markers
folders
scissors
glue sticks
pencils

100 200 300 400 500 600 700 800 900

Add or subtract. Use the graph to help solve each problem.

A. Mrs. Randolph's class used 523 pencils. How many are left?

B. Mr. Kirk's class used 156 scissors. How many are left?

C. Mr. Dean's class took 248 folders. Mr. Bhola's class took 176 folders. How many did they take altogether?

How many folders are left?

D. Mrs. Fenton's class used 96 glue sticks. Ms. Kwan's class used 189 glue sticks. How many did they use altogether?

How many glue sticks are left?

E. Mrs. Barry's class needs 275 markers. Mr. Lopez's class needs 398 markers. How many do they need altogether?

How many markers are left?

Name _____

Adding/subtracting 3-digit numbers with regrouping

Movie Madness

Add or subtract to solve.

A. 168 people are in line to buy tickets. 159 seats are available in the theatre. How many people will not get a ticket to the movie? ☐

B. 427 people attended the rush hour show. 289 people attended the 7:00 show. How many attended both shows altogether? ☐

C. 507 people ordered a popcorn and a soda. 278 people ordered popcorn only. How many more people ordered a soda? ☐

D. 319 people bought a pretzel. 299 people bought a box of candy. How many pretzels and candy were sold altogether? ☐

E. There were 826 people at the movie theatre on Friday. On Saturday, there were 697 people. How many more people were at the movie theatre on Friday? ☐

F. 258 people ordered a hot dog with mustard. 273 people ordered a hot dog with ketchup. How many hot dogs were ordered in all? ☐

Name _____

Animal Facts

Add or subtract.

T	O	L	P	A	W	I
247 + 253	463 + 440	217 + 68	639 + 207	391 + 144	459 + 492	198 + 672
P 842 − 314	**L** 504 + 475	**I** 500 − 293	**R** 457 + 364	**I** 903 − 339	**O** 107 + 147	**A** 924 − 71
N 700 − 427	**N** 903 − 34	**R** 703 − 186	**H** 258 + 553	**A** 357 + 537		

Move across each row. Write the letter from each box with the correct number of hundreds.

 2 hundreds — I am a cat that likes to sleep 20 hours a day.

5 hundreds — I have four toes on my front feet and three toes on my back feet.

8 hundreds — I am a fish with razor-sharp teeth.

9 hundreds — I can see well at night but cannot move my eyes.

Very Special Helpers

Add or subtract. Write the letter that goes with each answer in the center.

	E	L	H	F	D	A
207 + 566	814 – 245	339 + 128	540 – 166	422 – 174	615 – 230	409 + 387

772
– 484

I
635
+ 199

___ ___ ___ ___ ___ ___ ___
248 834 800 569 689 796 288

596
+ 287

M
841
– 152

___ ___ ___ ___ ___ ___ ___
896 569 796 259 374 569 800

___ ___ ___ ___ ___ ___
385 883 259 896 883 800

600
– 341

T
478
+ 418

___ ___ ___ ___ ___ ___ ___ ___ ___
467 834 773 800 796 800 834 796 288

603
+ 197

P
416
+ 288

___ ___ ___ ___ ___ ___ ___ ___ ___
704 883 467 834 259 569 689 796 288

Vacation Time

Write the name and the price of each item in the correct suitcase.
Add the prices.

$.77

$7.14

Beach

$ _____
$ _____
$ _____
$ _____

Total $ _____

$2.10

$6.89

Mountains

$ _____
$ _____
$ _____
$ _____

Total $ _____

$1.23

$1.23

$1.46

$3.74

**How much more does it cost to fill the mountain suitcase than the beach suitcase?
Show your work on a piece of paper.**

Bull's-eye

Select any problem. Add or subtract. Colour the answer on the target.
Repeat until you hit the bull's-eye. Then answer the remaining problems.

486
+ 294

653
− 187

343
+ 287

481

681

743

258

109   780

630   524

466   138

800
− 276

404
− 146

628
− 519

680
− 199

347
+ 396

974
− 836

505
+ 176

Write how many "tries" it took for you to hit the bull's-eye.

Grid Math

	A	B	C	D
3	550	636	282	963
2	189	148	579	415
1	427	751	370	804

Find the numbers on the grid. Add or subtract.

(A, 1) + (C, 3)

(B, 3) – (A, 3)

(D, 3) – (A, 2)

(B, 2) + (C, 1)

(A, 3) + (C, 1)

(D, 1) – (B, 3)

(A, 2) + (B, 1)

(C, 2) – (C, 3)

(D, 3) – (B, 2)

(D, 2) + (A, 2)

Perfect Punt

Add or subtract. Draw a line to connect each football to its goalpost.

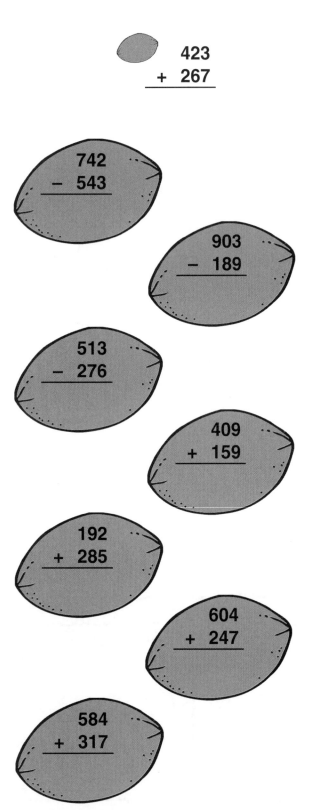

423
+ 267

742
− 543

903
− 189

513
− 276

409
+ 159

192
+ 285

604
+ 247

584
+ 317

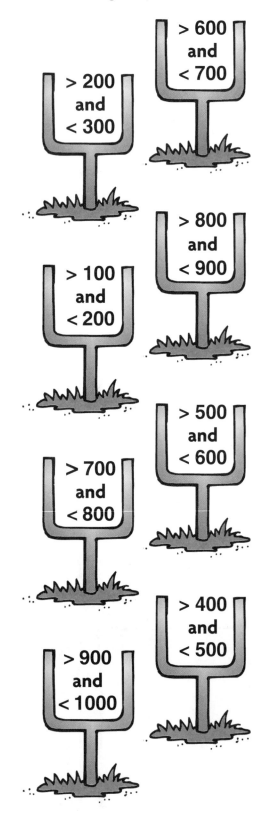

> 200
and
< 300

> 600
and
< 700

> 100
and
< 200

> 800
and
< 900

> 700
and
< 800

> 500
and
< 600

> 900
and
< 1000

> 400
and
< 500

Tic-Tac-Toe

How to Play:

1. Solve the problems in the first row of a game.

2. Mark the gameboard with an X or O for the largest answer.

3. Continue to solve the problems in each row to try to get three in a row.

Game 1

X	O
374 + 263	429 + 187
154 + 199	740 − 286
643 + 208	341 + 459
973 − 784	514 − 188
291 + 263	445 + 375

Game 2

X	O
166 + 117	149 + 69
801 − 389	722 − 305
318 + 218	266 + 243
576 + 268	607 + 266
629 − 457	785 − 657

Scholastic Success With

MATH

Name _____

Lone Donor

This is a number line. The numbers increase as you go along the line.

Mystery Critter

I climb up the side of walls and never fall.

I am a fast runner and have a very long tail. Who am I? _____

To find out, connect the numbers in order from 20 to 68.

Order Recorder

Can you identify numbers that come before, between, and after other numbers?

WRITE THE MISSING NUMBERS.

1. 64, 65, 66, ____
2. 33, ____, ____
3. 41, ____, ____, 44

4. 15, ____, 17, ____, 19
5. ____, ____, ____, 76
6. 29, 30, ____, ____, 33

WRITE WHAT COMES NEXT.

7. 2   4   6   8   ____ ____ ____ ____

8. 3   6   9   12   ____ ____ ____ ____

WRITE THE NUMBERS BETWEEN 82 AND 89.

9. 82 ____, ____, ____, ____, ____, ____, 89

WRITE **before** OR **after**.

10. ROOM 479 COMES _____ ROOM 478.

11. PAGE 53 COMES _____ PAGE 63.

12. 15th STREET COMES _____ 12th STREET.

13. AISLE 7 COMES _____ AISLE 12.

14. JUNE 29 COMES _____ JUNE 30.

15. EXIT 15 COMES _____ EXIT 22.

Missing Bone

McAllister the Mutt is dog-tired from walking in circles trying to find his bone. To help him find the path to the bone, move one paw print at a time in any direction except diagonally. You can only follow the tracks that have odd numbers. Draw a line to show his route.

Patterns for the Mail Carrier

Meimei the mail carrier is delivering letters. Give her some help.
Fill in the missing addresses on the houses below.

Extra

What pattern do you see in the house numbers?

_____

_____

_____

Amused Chooser

Compare numbers: > means greater than. < means less than. = means same as. Hint: The arrow points to the number that is less.

Write > < or = in the circles.

1. 11 ◯ 21   5. 59 ◯ 59

2. 56 ◯ 72   6. 38 ◯ 17

3. 47 ◯ 47   7. 526 ◯ 527

4. 64 ◯ 10   8. 159 ◯ 42

Fill in the blanks with numbers.

9. _____ < _____   13. _____ = _____

10. _____ < _____   14. _____ < _____

11. _____ > _____   15. _____ = _____

12. _____ < _____   16. _____ = _____

Write the numbers from greatest to least.

17. 37 54 61 73 _____

18. 22 96 43 24 _____

19. 79 78 69 51 _____

20. 15 27 51 37 _____

Name _____ **Place value**

Riddle Fun

What wears shoes, sandals, and boots, but has no feet?

A __ __ __ __ __ __ __ __

To find out, write each number in standard form. Then look for the numbers in the puzzle and circle them. They are written up, down, and backward. When you have circled all the numbers given, the letters in the blocks left uncircled spell the answer to the riddle. The first number has been circled for you.

4	3	2	1	9	9	5
B	A	R	K	S	I	G
8	1	7	1	7	5	6
R	M	Y	S	O	D	T
8	5	1	8	9	1	4
D	W	E	T	E	S	S
1	6	2	5	3	3	9
W	P	C	X	A	Z	P
4	9	7	7	0	7	0
L	J	F	S	R	M	L
8	3	6	9	2	0	9
H	F	Y	K	T	E	Q

8 ones 1 ten = 5 hundreds	518	5 ones 1 ten = 3 hundreds		6 ones 7 tens = 2 hundreds		3 ones 9 tens = 6 hundreds	
7 ones 3 tens = 1 hundred		4 ones 6 tens = 5 hundreds		9 ones 0 tens = 9 hundreds		1 one 1 ten = 8 hundreds	
9 ones 0 tens = 2 hundreds		7 ones 1 ten = 7 hundreds		6 ones 3 tens = 8 hundreds		1 one 2 tens = 3 hundreds	
8 ones 8 tens = 4 hundreds		7 ones 5 tens = 8 hundreds		2 ones 3 tens = 4 hundreds		7 ones 0 tens = 7 hundreds	

Name _____

Pattern Learner

A pattern is a repeated arrangement of numbers, shapes, or lines in a row. Continue the patterns below.

1. 324, 435, 546,

8. 11:05, 11:10, 11:15,

7. A C E G I K

Name _____

Combining shapes

Shape Tricks

Danny's class was learning about shapes. He noticed that you could draw a line across one shape to make two shapes. Draw a line through each shape below to make two new shapes. (Pattern blocks may help you.)

1. Make a square and a triangle.

2. Make two triangles.

3. Make two rectangles.

4. Make a triangle and a diamond.

5. Cut this twice to make 3 triangles.

Name _____

Picking Out Patterns

On the 100th day of school, everyone in Pat's class picked out patterns on the 100 Chart. Look at the chart below.

1	2	3	4	5	6	7	8	9	10
11	12	13	14	15	16	17	18	19	20
21	22	23	24	25	26	27	28	29	30
31	32	33	34	35	36	37	38	39	40
41	42	43	44	45	46	47	48	49	50
51	52	53	54	55	56	57	58	59	60
61	62	63	64	65	66	67	68	69	70
71	72	73	74	75	76	77	78	79	80
81	82	83	84	85	86	87	88	89	90
91	92	93	94	95	96	97	98	99	100

Find and finish the pattern starting with 2, 12, 22

_____

Find and finish the pattern starting with 100, 90, 80

_____

Find and finish the pattern starting with 97, 87, 77

_____

Find and finish the pattern starting with 11, 22, 33

_____

Shape Study

A heptagon has 7 sides. On a heptagon, all the sides are the same length.

Connect the dots in the geoboards below to make other shapes with 7 sides.

Shape Gaper

FLAT SHAPES HAVE LENGTH AND WIDTH.

A SQUARE   B CIRCLE   C RECTANGLE   D TRIANGLE

SOLID SHAPES HAVE LENGTH AND WIDTH AND DEPTH.

E CUBE   F SPHERE   G CYLINDER   H CONE   I RECTANGULAR PRISM   J PYRAMID

MATCH THE SHAPES WITH THESE OBJECTS. USE THE LETTERS ABOVE.

A.
1. BALL
2. WASTEBASKET
3. RING
4. POSTAGE STAMP
5. BIRDHOUSE
6. CRAYON BOX
7. ICE CUBE
8. PARTY HAT
9. GARBAGE CAN
10. JAR
11. ENVELOPE

B.
1. PIZZA
2. AN ORANGE
3. A PEN ANT
4. A BUILDING
5. FISH BOWL
6. CHILD'S BLOCK
7. CHECKERS (GAME)
8. A SAIL ON A SMALL BOAT
9. CEREAL BOX
10. PLANET EARTH
11. STICK OF BUTTER

C.
1. PYLON
2. FLAG
3. SHEET OF PAPER
4. FLASHLIGHT
5. SOUP CAN
6. POSTER
7. BASEBALL
8. TRAIN CAR
9. A DIME
10. PHOTOGRAPH
11. WORLD GLOBE

Rocket Riddle

What did the rocket say when it left the party?

What to Do

To find the answer to the riddle, solve the multiplication problems. Then match each product with a letter in the Key below. Write the correct letters on the blanks below.

1 **5 x 1** = _____

2 **8 x 1** = _____

3 **11 x 1** = _____

4 **26 x 1** = _____

5 **3 x 2** = _____

6 **5 x 2** = _____

7 **6 x 2** = _____

8 **8 x 2** = _____

9 **9 x 2** = _____

10 **12 x 2** = _____

Key

10 .... F		27 .... U		20 .... W	
13 C		8 .... E		7 .... D	
11 .... O		6 .... K		12 .... T	
16 .... E		9 .... B		26 .... O	
5 .... A		24 .... F		18 .... T	

Riddle Answer: "TIM ___ ___ ___ ___ ___ ___ ___ ___ ___ ___."

Wise Owls

What did the owl say when someone knocked on its door?

What to Do

To find the answer to the riddle, solve the multiplication problems. Then match each product with a letter in the Key below. Write the correct letters on the blanks below.

1 5 x 3 = _____

2 2 x 3 = _____

3 8 x 3 = _____

4 4 x 3 = _____

5 9 x 3 = _____

6 6 x 3 = _____

7 10 x 3 = _____

8 12 x 3 = _____

9 11 x 3 = _____

10 0 x 3 = _____

Key

30 .... O	8 .... K	42 .... N
11 .... A	15 0	24 .... T
36 .... H	0 I	33 0
18 I	27 0	6 .... Q
32 .... F	6 .... S	12 .... W

Riddle
Answer: " ___ ___ ___ ___ ___ ___ ___ ___ ___ ___ ?"

④ ⑧ ⑤ ⑨ ① ⑦   ⑩ ②   ⑥ ③

Jack's Beanstalk

Jack's class was growing bean plants.
After 1 week, Jack's was the tallest.
Measure Jack's plant below. Record its height: _____ cm
After 2 weeks, Jack's plant had doubled in height.
How tall was it now? _____ cm

Draw a picture to show how tall the plant grew.

Measure your drawing to make sure it is the correct height.

2 weeks.

After 3 weeks, Jack's plant was still growing!

How tall would it be now? _____ cm

Explain your answer. _____

_____

Candy Boxes

Steve works in a candy store. He puts candy into boxes. Each box has 10 spaces. Steve has 32 candies. Try to draw 32 candies in the boxes below. Write the number of candies in each box on the line. Write the number of any leftover candy at the bottom of the page.

Extra

Leftover candies: _____

Creature Categories

Nick's class took a field trip to the beach. When they looked in the tide pools, they saw a lot of animals. Group the animals they saw. Colour the animals in each group the same colour.

Write a word or phrase that explains how you grouped them.

Group #1 _____

Group #2 _____

Group #3 _____

Coin-Toss Addition

Toss 8 coins. Write "**H**" for heads or "**T**" for tails in the circles below to show your toss. Then write the addition equation. Write the number of "heads" first. We did the first one for you. Try it three times.

(**H**) (**H**) (**H**) (**H**) (**T**) (**T**) (**T**) (**T**)

Equation: _____ **4 + 4 = 8** _____

Equation: _____

Equation: _____

Equation: _____

Clear Reader

Write each sentence using numbers and symbols.

1. Four plus five is nine.	
2. Eleven minus six is five.	
3. Nine plus seven is sixteen.	
4. Four plus eight is twelve.	
5. Three minus two is one.	
6. Seven plus seven is fourteen.	
7. Fifteen minus ten is five.	
8. Two plus eight is ten.	
9. Five minus two is three.	

Time to Get Up!

Twenty animals were hibernating near Sleepy Pond.
5 of them woke up. Colour 5 animals below.

How many are still sleeping? _____

A week later, 7 more woke up. Colour 7 other animals.

How many are still sleeping? _____

Pizza Party

Garth's class is having a pizza party. They made a diagram to show which pizzas they would like. Draw an X in each circle to show how many classmates wanted each kind of pizza.

- 5 wanted cheese pizza.
- 10 wanted pepperoni pizza.
- 3 wanted sausage pizza.
- 2 wanted both cheese and pepperoni pizza.

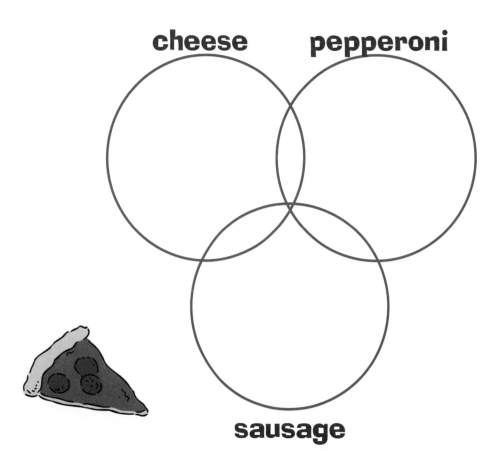

cheese   **pepperoni**

sausage

What can you learn by looking at this diagram? Write your ideas:

_____

_____

Prime Timer

WRITE THE TIME 3 WAYS.

example: ← 1:15
15 minutes after 1
45 minutes to 2

1. _____

_____ minutes after _____

_____ minutes to _____

2. _____

_____ minutes after _____

_____ minutes to _____

3. _____

_____ minutes after _____

_____ minutes to _____

4. _____

_____ minutes after _____

_____ minutes to _____

5. _____

_____ minutes after _____

_____ minutes to _____

6. _____

_____ minutes after _____

_____ minutes to _____

Just Snacks

Use the menu on page 369 to answer the
following questions.

1. **Which snack costs the most?**

   _____

   How much do they cost?

   _____

2. **Which sweet costs the least?** _____

   How much does it cost? _____

3. **Li spends 50¢ on a snack.**

   What does he buy? _____

4. **Gina orders a drink. She spends 15¢.**

   Which drink does she order? _____

5. **Dan orders popcorn and a cookie.**

   How much does he pay? _____

6. **Pat buys a cup of soup and a sip of milk.**

   How much does she spend? _____

Name _____

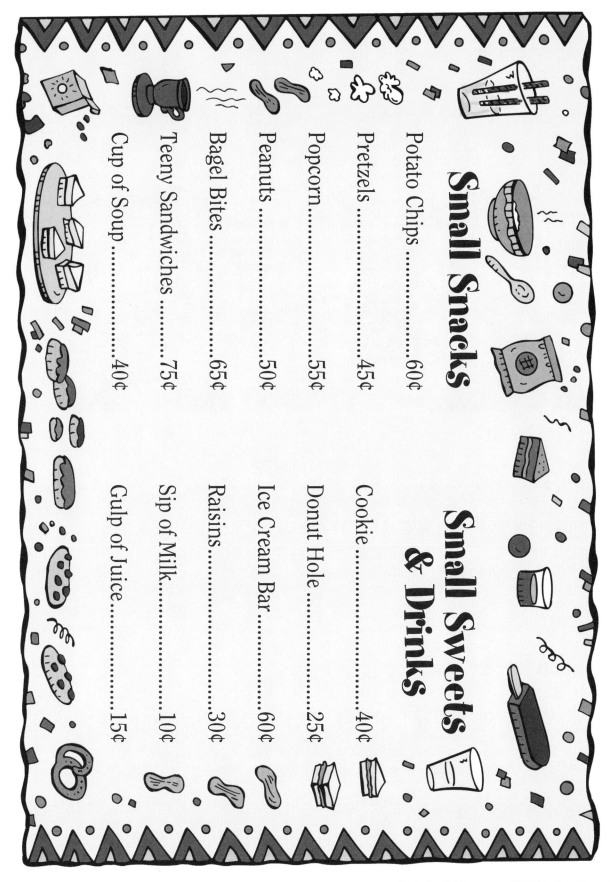

Small Snacks

Potato Chips ....60¢

Pretzels ....45¢

Popcorn ....55¢

Peanuts ....50¢

Bagel Bites ....65¢

Teeny Sandwiches ....75¢

Cup of Soup ....40¢

Small Sweets & Drinks

Cookie ....40¢

Donut Hole ....25¢

Ice Cream Bar ....60¢

Raisins ....30¢

Sip of Milk ....10¢

Gulp of Juice ....15¢

Comparing coins
and amounts

Money Matters

Alex asked his little brother Billy to trade piggy banks.

Alex's bank has these coins: **Billy's has these coins:**

Do you think this is a fair trade? _____

Test your answer:

Add up Alex's coins: _____

Add up Billy's coins: _____

Write the totals in this Greater Than/Less Than equation:

_____ > _____

Who has more money? _____

Best Estimator

LENGTH CAN BE MEASURED IN CENTIMETRES, METRES AND KILOMETRES. 100 CENTIMETRES = 1 METRE. 1000 METRES = 1 KILOMETRE.

UNDERLINE THE MORE SENSIBLE MEASURE.

How many CENTIMETRES to Vancouver, Sir?

BUS STOP

7. LENGTH OF A FOOTBALL FIELD
   CENTIMETRES   METRES

8. DISTANCE FROM EARTH TO MOON
   KILOMETRES   METRES

9. DEPTH OF A SWIMMING POOL
   METRES   CENTIMETRES

1. HEIGHT OF A BOOKCASE
   CENTIMETRES   METRES

10. TUBE OF TOOTHPASTE
    CENTIMETRES   METRES

2. WIDTH OF YOUR BACKYARD
   METRES   KILOMETRES

11. HEIGHT OF A REFRIGERATOR
    CENTIMETRES   METRES

3. LENGTH OF A RIVER
   KILOMETRES   METRES

12. WIDTH OF A BEDROOM
    METRES   CENTIMETRES

4. WIDTH OF A DESK
   CENTIMETRES   METRES

13. DISTANCE BETWEEN 2 CITIES
    KILOMETRES   METRES

5. LENGTH OF YOUR ARM
   METRES   CENTIMETRES

14. LENGTH OF A DOLLAR
    CENTIMETRES   METRES

6. LENGTH OF A COMB
   CENTIMETRES   METRES

15. LENGTH OF AN AUTOMOBILE
    CENTIMETRES   METRES

December Weather

In December, Mrs. Monroe's class drew the weather on a calendar. Each kind of weather has a picture:

| sunny | cloudy | rainy | snowy |

Look at the calendar. Answer the questions below.

How many sunny days did they have? _____

How many cloudy days did they have? _____

How many rainy days did they have? _____

How many snowy days did they have? _____

Which kind of weather did they have the most? _____

Name _____

Measuring Perimeter

Use a ruler to measure each side of each triangle in centimetres. Write the centimetres (cm) in the spaces below. Then add up all the sides to find the perimeter, or distance around each triangle.

____ + ____ + ____ = ____ cm

____ + ____ + ____ = ____ cm

____ + ____ + ____ = ____ cm

Night-Light

1. Find each number pair on the graph. Make a dot for each.
2. Connect the dots in the order that you make them.
3. What picture did you make?

_____

	Across	Up
1.	6	11
2.	5	7
3.	1	7
4.	4	5
5.	3	0
6.	6	3
7.	9	0
8.	8	5
9.	11	7
10.	7	7
11.	6	11

Great Graphing

The picture was made with 7 different shapes. How many of each shape was used? Colour in the shapes, following the instructions. Then colour in the boxes on the chart, 1 box for each shape used.

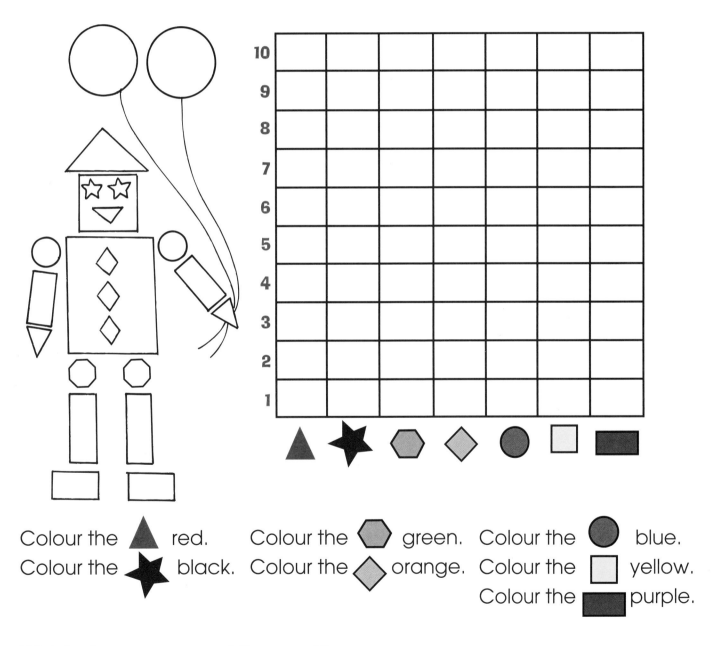

Colour the ▲ red.   Colour the ⬡ green.   Colour the ● blue.

Colour the ★ black.   Colour the ◆ orange.   Colour the ▢ yellow.

Colour the ▬ purple.

Which shape was used the most? _____

Fruit Graph

Ask 12 friends which of these four fruits they like most. Fill in the graph to find out. Colour one box on the graph for each vote.

Which fruit was the most popular? _____

How many votes did it get? _____

Which fruit was the least popular? _____

How many votes did it get? _____

If two fruits got the same amount of votes, they "tied."

Write any ties below.

_____ and _____

_____ and _____

Chester's Cakes and Pies

Fill in the blanks. Chester Chipmunk was cutting cakes and pies.
Bobby Bear said, "Some aren't cut in half. When you cut something in
half, there are _____ pieces and both of the pieces are the
same _____."
Here is how Chester cut the cakes and pies.
Circle the desserts that are cut in half correctly.

Part Timer

Determine fractions of a whole. Check √ your answers.

1. HOW MUCH JUICE IS LEFT?

$\frac{1}{2}$
$\frac{1}{4}$
$\frac{1}{3}$

2. HOW MUCH PIZZA IS GONE?

$\frac{1}{2}$
$\frac{1}{3}$
$\frac{1}{8}$

3. HOW MUCH HAS BEEN EATEN?

$\frac{1}{3}$
$\frac{1}{6}$
$\frac{1}{4}$

4. HOW MUCH IS GONE?

$\frac{1}{4}$
$\frac{1}{2}$
$\frac{1}{6}$

5. HOW MUCH IS LACED?

$\frac{1}{2}$
$\frac{1}{3}$
$\frac{1}{4}$

6. HOW MUCH TONIC IS LEFT?

$\frac{1}{6}$
$\frac{1}{4}$
$\frac{1}{3}$

7. HOW MUCH WATER IS LEFT?

$\frac{3}{4}$
$\frac{1}{2}$
$\frac{1}{4}$

8. HOW MUCH HAS BEEN CUT OFF?

$\frac{1}{2}$ $\frac{1}{4}$
$\frac{1}{3}$

9. HOW MUCH WATER REMAINS?

$\frac{3}{4}$ $\frac{1}{2}$ $\frac{1}{4}$

10. HOW MUCH LEAF HAS BEEN EATEN?

$\frac{1}{4}$
$\frac{1}{6}$
$\frac{2}{3}$

11. HOW MUCH BREAD IS UNCUT?

$\frac{1}{4}$ $\frac{1}{3}$ $\frac{1}{2}$

Name _____

Fraction Fun

Something that is split in 2 equal parts is divided in "half."

These two shapes are divided in half.

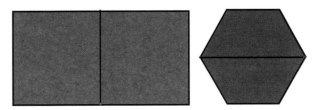

A fraction has a number on the top: ⟶ **1**

A fraction has a number on the bottom, too: ⟶ **2**

The top number tells the "fraction," or parts, of the whole.

The bottom number tells the number of parts in the whole.

Draw a line to match the picture with a fraction.

$$\frac{2}{2} \qquad \frac{2}{12} \qquad \frac{2}{3}$$

The top number in these fractions tells you how many parts to colour. Try it!

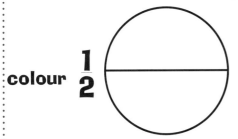

colour $\frac{1}{2}$ colour $\frac{2}{2}$

Name _____

Fun With Fractions

A fraction has two numbers. The top number will tell you how many parts to colour. The bottom number tells you how many parts there are.

Colour 1/5 of the circle.

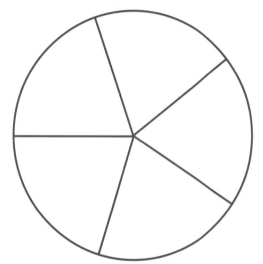

Colour 4/5 of the rectangle.

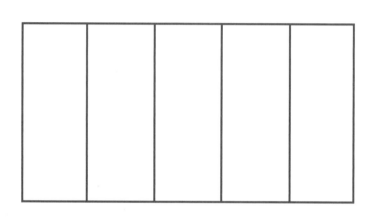

Colour 3/5 of the ants.

Colour 2/5 of the spiders.

Colour 0/5 of the bees.

Colour 5/5 of the worms.

More Fun With Fractions

A fraction has two numbers. The top number will tell you how many parts to colour. The bottom number tells you how many total parts there are.

$\frac{10}{10}$ is the whole circle.

$\frac{10}{10}$ is the whole rectangle.

Colour $\frac{8}{10}$ of the circle.

Colour $\frac{4}{10}$ of the rectangle.

How much is not coloured? _____

How much is not coloured? _____

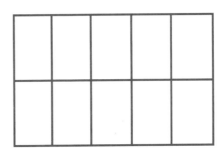

$\frac{10}{10} - \frac{8}{10} = \underline{\quad}$

$\frac{10}{10} - \frac{4}{10} = \underline{\quad}$

Solve this fraction equation. Cross out the dogs to help you.

$$\frac{10}{10} - \frac{3}{10} = \underline{\quad}$$

Answer Key

Reading Comprehension

Page 12
1. spots; My domino has two white spots, and yours has five. 2. sea bird; A grey seabird flew by the cruise ship. 3. A green stone; The queen had a beautiful necklace made of a green stone. 4. flute player; My sister is the best flute player in the high school band.

Page 13
Neil Armstrong was the first man to walk on the moon.

Page 14
1. IOU; 2. OK; 3. ICU; 4. AB; 5. MT; 6. IV

Page 15
Police officers help people.

Page 16
On Saturday, Rachel got up early. Mom was still asleep, so Rachel made her own breakfast. She put some peanut butter in a bowl. She mixed it with a little *honey. Then she stirred in some *oatmeal, *bran flakes, and *raisins. It tasted yummy! When Mom got up, she said, "Oh, You made granola!"

Page 17
1. B; 2. U; 3. L; 4. L; 5. R ; 6. I; 7. D; 8. E; 9. R ; 10. S; Bullriders

Page 18

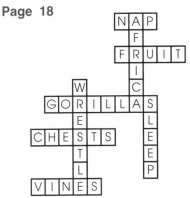

Page 19
Make-believe: pig, goat and sheep, horses, pizza and hamburgers, mouse and table, golden eggs, crickets (The others are real.)

Page 20
Real: a woman feeding animals; a grandmother living alone; sleeping on hay in a barn; a house burning down; crying that her house burned (The rest are make-believe.)

Page 21
Children's answers will vary.

Page 22
1. Mia begged Spooky to come down. 2. Mia asked Mr. Carson for help. 3. Mr. Carson called his firefighter friends. 4. The fire truck came. 5. A firefighter climbed the ladder. 6. Spooky jumped to a tree and climbed down. 7. Mia scolded Spooky. 8. The firefighters laughed.

Page 23
Writing; Math; Recess; Social Studies; 11:00; Story Time; Science; Spelling; Music

Page 24
3, 1, 4, 2, 6, 7, 5, 8

Page 25
(Child's name) knows how to follow directions!

Page 26
Check child's picture.

Page 27
1. math; 2. taking out the trash; 3. playing a video game; 4. going to bed

Page 28
1. Backward Day
2. Check child's dot-to-dot picture.
3. 50, 45, 40, 35, 30, 25, 20, 15, 10, 5

Page 29
1. stealing; paid for it; 2. showed bad manners; said "Excuse me"; 3. lying; told the truth; 4. hurt his feelings; helped him

Page 30
Each tree should be illustrated as described in the story.

Page 31
1. box shape; 2. heart shape; 3. circle shape; 4. semi-circle shape; 5. arc shape

Page 32
1. Zolak's shadow; 2. No; 3. No; He didn't see any real earthling, only his own shadow.

4.

Page 33
1, 4, 6, 7, 10, 11, 14, 15, 18, 20, 21, 24, 26, teapot

Page 34
People Who Went to the Beach: Dad, Mom, Tim, and Tara

What They Did: swam, fished, built sandcastles, went sailing

Picnic Items: ham sandwiches, potato chips, apples, cookies, lemonade

Living Things They Saw on the Beach: crab, dog, starfish, sea gulls

Page 35
1. cheerful; angry; 2. away; west; 3. goat; parakeet; 4. mud; lemonade; 5. toy; arm; 6. Sarah; George; 7. spinach; pudding; 8. bicycle; crayon; 9. marble; loonie

Birds 3; Desserts 7; Bad Feelings 1; Boys' Names 6; Money 9; School Supplies 8; Directions 2; Body Parts 5; Drinks 4

Page 36
Answers will vary.

Page 37
1. He learned to fly. 2. All of a sudden something wonderful happened. 3. afraid; 4. proud

Page 38
(Accept any reasonable answers.)
1. The home team wins the game. 2. The brownies will burn. 3. She will have a flat tire. 4. It will rain. 5. Mom will fall. 6. The boat will sink.

Page 39
Child should draw pictures that show these conclusions: Rita became a rabbit again. Diana became a duck again.

Page 40
Ryan—giant tortoise, 3-toed sloth
Both—albino alligator
Mariam—giraffe, owl

Page 41
Each had twenty dollars to spend. Joey bought sweets. Harry bought breakfast food.

Page 42
both, Kendra, Lacey, Lacey, both, Lacey, Lacey, Kendra, Lacey, Kendra, Lacey

Page 43

Things made of cotton: shirt, pillow, sock, shorts, towel.

not made of cotton: scissors, pitcher, trumpet, cake

Page 44

Page 45
1. spewing hot lava and ash into the air; 2. for people and animals to breathe; 3. flattened trees; 4. forest fires; 5. floods and mudslides; 6. it still erupts from time to time

Page 46
Check children's work to be sure they have correctly identified stage directions.

Page 47
1. Man; Lady; 2. hot dogs; chicken nuggets; 3. frowns; smiles; 4. Miss Daniels; Lunch Lady; 5. hardware; shoe; 6. mean; kind

Page 48
The girls got too loud, so Dad said to be quiet. The girls saw a bee land on Dad's bald head, so Mary Beth whopped Dad on the head with a book. The car ran off the road and through a fence, which let the cows out.

Page 49
1. 3
6. Dr. Smileyface makes his patients laugh. 7. The child who wrote this story is not afraid to go to the dentist. 8. Dr. Smileyface teaches kids how to take care of their teeth. 9. Dr. Smileyface sends kids home with a surprise.

Page 50
HELPING OTHERS

Page 51
Children should circle Jed, bed and head. They should draw a box around long and wrong.
Daisy, lazy, class, pass, crazy

Page 52
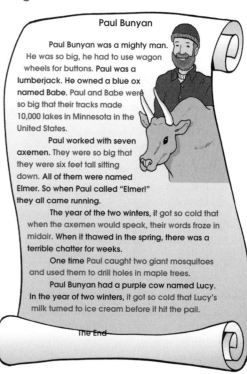

Tests: Reading
Pages 57–60   Test 1

A. Phonic Analysis: Consonants
Sample: cat
1. window 2. geese
3. ship 4. dog 5. lamp
6. hat 7. teeth 8. truck

B. Dictation
Sample: cat
1. window 2. geese 3. ship

C. Vocabulary: Picture-Word Match
Sample: girl
1. leaf 2. barn 3. moon
4. boy 5. mouse

D. High-Frequency Word Match
Sample: the
1. or 2. from 3. have
4. where 5. through

E. Grammar, Usage and Mechanics
Sample: He ran up the hill.

1. Did you take that book home?
2. We played outside all day.
3. Mrs. Smith is our teacher this year.
4. Maria is in my class.
5. I didn't have any homework last week.

F. Story Comprehension
1. in ponds   2. Frogs
3. a frog   4. bugs

Pages 61–64   Test 2

A. Phonic Analysis: Consonants
Sample: car

1. block   2. train   3. nest 4. bat
5. fish

B. Phonic Analysis: Vowels
Sample: cheese

1. broom   2. coat 3. mouse
4. three   5. bike

C. Dictation
Sample: cheese

1. broom   2. coat   3. mouse

D. High-Frequency Word Match
Sample: where

1. off   2. very   3. know 4. could
5. something

E. Grammar, Usage and Mechanics
Sample: He plays in the park.

1. Did you see that star? 2. We run in the yard.
3. Mr. Smith is my neighbour.
4. She moved to Toronto.
5. He can't come to my house today.
6. Watch out!
7. The dog chased the cat.
8. Dr. Hamilton is nice.
9. We went to Alberta.

F. Story Comprehension
1. groups of whales 2. Whales
3. stay wet 4. to get air

Pages 65–68   Test 3

A. Phonic Analysis: Consonants
Sample: car

1. bed   2. clock   3. grapes
4. hand   5. tooth

B. Phonic Analysis: Vowels
Sample: boat

1. house   2. feet   3. spoon
4. train   5. kite

C. Dictation
Sample: boat

1. house   2. feet   3. spoon

D. High Frequency Word Match
Sample: there

1. about   2. should   3. those
4. knew   5. everything

E. Grammar, Usage and Mechanics
Sample: They walk to school.

1. I ride my bike in the park.
2. Can you lift this box?
3. My friend's name is Peter Jones.
4. We live in Manitoba.
5. Be careful!
6. I don't want to play.
7. We played at his house.
8. She's on her way home.
9. Our family doctor is Dr. Levchuck.

F. Story Comprehension
1. Tornadoes   2. a tornado
3. on hot days   4. to be safe

Pages 69–72   Test 4

A. Phonic Analysis: Consonants
Sample: broom

1. flag   2. spoon   3. snake
4. ring   5. truck

B. Phonic Analysis: Vowels
Sample: bike

1. coat   2. cake   3. leaf 4. rain
5. couch

C. Phonemic Awareness
Sample: pencil —2

1. tomato—3   2. map—1
3. information—4
4. bookmark—2   5. elephant—3

D. High-Frequency Word Match
Sample: who

1. after   2. school   3. because
4. might   5. know

E. Grammar, Usage and Mechanics
Sample: We walk to school.

1. The boys colour their pictures.
2. Yesterday, I played with my friend.
3. What is in your bag?
4. Look out!
5. My dog won't run.
6. She's going to the fair.
7. My mother will buy me a new coat next week.
8. I went on a trip to Nunavut.
9. Dr. Singh gave me a checkup.

F. Story Comprehension
1. Tigers   2. deer and wild pigs
3. Asia   4. Answers will vary

Pages 73–76   Test 5

A. Phonic Analysis: Consonants
Sample: tree

1. chair   2. plane   3. snake
4. nest   5. fish

B. Phonic Analysis: Vowels
Sample: baby

1. house   2. goat   3. zebra
4. spider   5. book

B. Dictation
Sample: baby

1. house   2. goat   3. zebra

D. High Frequency Word Match
1. which   2. off   3. every   4. knot
5. will   6. together

E. Grammar, Usage and Mechanics
Sample: She ran in the park.

1. Did you read that book?
2. We swam in the lake.
3. Dr. Bell is my dentist.
4. She lives in Centreville.
5. He won't be at the soccer game.
6. Watch out!
7. The rabbit hopped to the carrot.
8. Mrs. Campbell drove the school bus.
9. We took a trip to Halifax.
10. I couldn't go to the park.

F. Story Comprehension
1. bird claws 2. Claws 3. to hold on to things 4. bear

Pages 77–80   Test 6

A. Phonic Analysis: Consonants
Sample: star

1. grapes 2. slide 3. branch
4. hand 5. clock

B. Phonic Analysis: Vowels
Sample: kite

1. boat 2. snake 3. pear
4. rainbow 5. cloud

C. Phonemic Awareness
Sample: apple—2

1. soup—1 2. cartwheel—2
3. television—4 4. shirt—1
5. animals—3

D. Grammar, Usage and Mechanics
Sample: She rides a horse.

1. The children play soccer.
2. Last night, we watched a great movie.
3. Which story is yours?
4. That frog won't jump.
5. He's going to the zoo.
6. My book will come in the mail tomorrow.
7. Ms. Cohen read a story to us.

E. Story Comprehension
1. Elephant Herds

2. a baby elephant
3. big and angry
4. Answers will vary

F. Story Comprehension
1. Chinese New Year
2. 15 days
3. cleaning their homes
4. Answers will vary.

Pages 81–84   Test 7

A. Phonic Analysis: Consonants
Sample: spider
1. watch 2. swan 3. plant
4. lock 5. box

B. Phonic Analysis: Vowels
Sample: baby

1. snail 2. iron 3. stove 4. ruler 5. boy

C. Phonemic Awareness
Sample: paper—2

1. elephant—3 2. ice—1
3. information—4 4. principal—3
5. apple—2

D. Grammar, Usage and Mechanics
Sample: They live in a city.

1. The farm animals eat grain.
2. Today, we will give the dog a bath.
3. Ouch! A bee stung me!
4. I can't swim in the deep water yet.
5. She's going to the library.
6. My aunt will take me to the movies tomorrow.
7. Mr. O'Connor fixed my bike.

E. Story Comprehension
1. Kwanzaa 2. 7 3. kind of candle-holder 4. Answers will vary.

F. Reading a Graph
1. how many teeth students have lost
2. 4 students 3. 7 4. 0

Pages 85–88   Test 8

A. Phonic Analysis: Consonants
Sample: star

1. whale 2. flower 3. three
4. desk 5. zebra

B. Phonic Analysis: Vowels
Sample: foot

1. wheel 2. cloud 3. radio
4. bread 5. pie

C. Grammar, Usage and Mechanics
Sample: We go to the park.

1. Can she run in the race?
2. They play baseball.
3. Mrs. Miller is my teacher.
4. She went on a trip to Calgary.
5. He couldn't drive the car.
6. Help! There is a fire!
7. My aunt lives in Montreal, Quebec.
8. "Let's eat out," said Mom.
9. The children can run around the track.

D. Story Comprehension
1. Trees Are Important 2. food
3. the fox 4. a baseball bat

E. Reading a Graph
1. what sports kids like best
2. soccer 3. 5
4. skating and baseball

Pages 89–92   Test 9

A. Phonic Analysis: Consonants
Sample: yarn

1. cheese 2. fish 3. tent
4. brush 5. clown

B. Phonic Analysis: Vowels
Sample: moon

1. house 2. feet 3. pear 4. fly
5. coin

C. Grammar, Usage and Mechanics
Sample: We race down the hill.

1. May I go to the store?
2. He plays football every day.
3. I saw Mrs. Walker at the park.
4. I will visit my grandma in March.
5. Wow! You hit the ball hard.
6. I can't run as fast as Sami.
7. "I'm on my way," said Jane.
8. Yesterday, we rode our bikes.
9. We will soon move to Ontario.

D. Story Comprehension

1. Night Animals

2. a strong sense of smell

3. see in the dark

4. to hide from other animals

E. Reading a Graph

1. what colors students like best
2. 6   3. red and green 4. 3

Pages 93–96   Test 10

A. Word-Match Dictation

Sample: I know the way to the playground.

1. We saw a deer in the woods.

2. Where do you want to go?

3. We got home last night.

4. I sent the letter yesterday.

5. Tim and Anna got mud on their clothes.

B. Synonyms

Sample: large

1. glad   2. quick   3. respond
4. fearless   5. furious

C. Antonyms

Sample: night

1. young   2. cold   3. dirty
4. short   5. weak

D. Grammar, Usage and Mechanics

Sample: The boy walked home.

1. Where do you live?

2. Maria and I play soccer.

3. Our teacher is Mr. Lee.

4. We will watch a movie tomorrow.

5. Trish turned 8 years old on February 22, 2017.

6. Yukon is in the north.

7. Yesterday, my mom helped me with my homework.

8. Owls don't sleep at night.

9. Jake is taller than Ed.

10. Is this your book?

11. We went for a ride in Mike's car.

E. Story and Graph Comprehension

1. twister   2. spring   3. 2014   4. 3

F. Story Comprehension

1. Hungry Spiders   2. animals

3. They eat insects that destroy crops.   4. Answers will vary.

Pages 97–100   Test 11

A. Word Match Dictation

Sample: Who won the game?

1. We built a sand castle.

2. I got mad at my brother.

3. Fill the pail with water.

4. Don't tear your jacket!

5. Did you hear the news?

B. Synonyms

Sample: centre

1. kid   2. close   3. see   4. tells
5. completed

C. Antonyms

Sample: few

1. mine   2. short   3. loud   4. shrink
5. less

D. Grammar, Usage and Mechanics

Sample: It is time for bed.

1. Did you brush your teeth?

2. Pam and I played with blocks.

3. School is over at three o'clock.

4. Today I will practise piano.

5. What do you want for your birthday?

6. Ottawa is where the Prime Minister lives.

7. Will you push me on the swing?

8. I am finished reading this book.

9. She can ride a horse.

10. Jack's brother will turn 5 on October 28th, 2022.

11. Tim's cat has kittens.

E. Story Comprehension

1. 300   2. brain   3. living cells
4. Your Bones

F. Story Comprehension

1. They are too far away to come home each night. 2. gravity
3. sleep in a sleeping bag strapped to the walls.

4. Answers will vary.

Grammar

Page 148

1. T   2. Q   3. Q   4. T   5. T
6. Q   7. T

Page 149

1. T,

2. S,

3. D, ?

4. I, ?

5. M, .

6. Will he take the cat home?

Page 150

1. correct as is   2. The vet   3. cats.
4. correct as is   5. Do you
6. When is   7. He has   8. the vet.
9. goldfish?   10. Will you

Page 151

1. E.   2. C   3. E   4. E   5. E
6. C   7. I'm upset!
8. Don't copy other people.

Page 152

1. fear   2. excitement   3. surprise
4. anger   5. Please don't be upset!
6. Answers will vary.
7. Answers will vary.

Page 153

1. You are a great hopper!

2. The picture looks beautiful!

3. I can paint, too!

4. correct as is

5. Teach me how to hop.

6. Hop backward like this.

Page 154

1. I, .   2. M, I, ?   3. I, !   4. C, I, ?
5. B, I, .

Telling Sentences: I sail my boat in the lake. Bill and I fly the kite.

Questions: May I have a turn? Can Kiku and I play?

Exclamations: I am so happy!

Page 155

1. T   2. C   3. T   4. C   5. Q
6. E   7. Q   8. I, Answers will vary.
9. I, Answers will vary.
10. I, Answers will vary.

Page 156
1. I have fun with my bike.
2. Can I ride to the beach?
3. I find a pretty shell.
4. correct as is
5. Get the shovel.
6. What a mess I made!

Page 157
1. boy, boat   2. brothers, park
3. girl, grandmother   4. boats, lake
5. Friends, needle, thread, sail
People: boy, brothers, girl, grandmother, friends
Places: park, lake
Things: boat, boats, needle, thread, sail

Page 158
Circled nouns: village, office, cane, pencil, doctor, boy, bed, aunt, school
People: doctor, boy, aunt
Places: village, school, office
Things: cane, pencil, bed

Page 159
1. no   2. yes   3. no   4. yes
5. place   6. person   7. person
8. thing

Page 160
1. George Ancona   2. Mexico
3. Jorgito   4. Vancouver
5. Honduras   6. Tio Mario
People: George Ancona, Jorgito, Tio Mario
Places: Mexico, Vancouver, Honduras

Page 161
1. Sue   2. California
3. Los Angeles   4. Pacific Ocean   5. Tonya   6. Sue Wong
7. Shore Road   8. Victoria
Answers will vary.

Page 162
1. person   2. place   3. person
4. place   5. Emilio   6. Florida
7. Disney World   8. Main Street

Page 163
1. runs   2. wears   3. smacks
4. holds   5. misses   6. waits

7. writes   8. helps

Page 164
1. watch   2. throws   3. opens
4. cheers   5. hits   6. runs   7. yells
8. eat

Page 165
1. action verb   2. not an action verb
3. not an action verb   4. not an action verb   5. action verb
6. action verb   7. not an action verb 8. action verb   9. action verb
10. not an action verb

Page 166
2. Crow, X   3. The water, X
6. One mouse, X

Page 167
1. a. Lin likes to play soccer.
2. b. Her friends watch her play.
3. a. They cheer for Lin.
4. a. Her mom goes to all of her games.
5. a. The coach is very proud of Lin.

Page 168
1. telling part   2. naming part
3. not the whole part   4. not the whole part   5. saw the cat go away
6. Then the bird   7. After a minute, the cat   8. walked back, too

Page 169
1. planted   2. watered   3. weeded
4. discovered   5. (blank)   6. pulled

Page 170
1. pushed   2. splashed   3. rolled
4. followed   5. washed
Answers will vary.

Page 171
1. visited   2. correct as is
3. correct as is   4. talked   5. asked
6. correct as is   7. correct as is
8. showed

Page 172
1. He, Wendell   2. She, Mother
3. They, The pigs   4. it, a board game   5. They, The pigs and Wendell   6. He, Wendell

Page 173
1. it   2. They   3. It   4. she   5. He

Page 174
1. Mrs. Fultz   2. The boy
3. The house   4. The pigs
5. He   6. they

Page 175
Exclamation: What a big mango! This tastes great!
Command: Buy me an avocado. Come over for dinner.
Question: Is that a banana? Did you find the fruit?
Telling Sentence: I want to eat dinner. I like mangoes.

Page 176
1. T   2. Q   3. T   4. C   5. E
6. C   7. Q   8. E

Page 177
1. command   2. question
3. exclamation   4. command
5. exclamation   6. telling
7. question   8. telling

Page 178
1. Two brothers can live together.
2. Hungbu will find a new home.
3. Mother will fix the house.
4. Will Sister clean the house?
5. Can the bird help them?

Page 179
1. Will I find some wood? QUESTION
2. Each of us must help. STATEMENT
3. Where are the trees? QUESTION
4. That is your pumpkin. Is that your pumpkin?
5. You can help cut the pumpkin. Can you help cut the pumpkin?

Page 180
1. Dad made eggs for breakfast.
2. He cracked open four eggs.
3. Do you like eggs?
4. Did you help him?
5. Beat eggs with a fork.
6. correct as is

Page 181
1. accordion(s) 2. brush(es)
3. clock(s), watch(es) 4. flower(s)
box(es) accordions, clocks, flowers
brushes, watches, boxes

Page 182
1. sandwiches 2. lunches
3. lunchboxes 4. dishes 5. boxes
6. dresses 7. coats 8. benches

Page 183
1. sketches 2. correct as is
3. foxes 4. correct as is
5. correct as is 6. dresses
7. balls 8. correct as is

Page 184
1. brown, heavy 2. striped, two
3. little, six 4. brown, heavy,
striped, little 5. two, six

Page 185
1. zoo, big 2. giraffe, tall 3. girls,
two 4. spots, brown

colour word: brown

size words: tall, big

number word: two

Page 186
1. red 2. yellow 3. purple 4. big
5. three 6. little 7. huge 8. Two

Page 187
1. is, now 2. are, now 3. were,
past 4. is, now 5. am, now
6. was, past

Page 188
1. is/was, one 2. is/was, one
3. were, more 4. are, more
5. was, one 6. are, more

Page 189
1. past, one
2. present, more than one
3. past, more than one
4. past, more than one
5. past, more than one
6. present, one

Page 190
1. present 2. present 3. present
4. present 5. past 6. past
7. past 8. past

Page 191
1. went 2. goes 3. does 4. did
5. Do 6. go

Page 192
1. goes 2. do 3. does 4. go
5. did 6. went 7. went 8. did

Page 193
1. "Let's go on a picnic."
2. "That's a great idea."
3. "What should we bring?"
4. "We should bring food."
5. "Yes, let's bring lots and lots of
food."
6. "You're no help at all!"
7. Answers will vary.

Page 194
1. "It is raining!"
2. "What will we do today?"
3. "We could read."
4. "Maybe the sun will come out
soon."
5. "But what will we do now?"
6. "Use your imagination!"
Answers will vary.

Page 195
1. "Let's make a sand castle," said
Lenny.
2. "Where's the pail and
shovel?" asked Sonya.
3. Sara said, "Maybe Otis can help."
4. "Do you want to dig?" asked
Lenny.
5. Sonya shouted, "Get some water!"
6. "Look what we made!" cried the
children.

Page 196
1. aren't, are not 2. doesn't, does
not 3. can't, cannot 4. couldn't,
could not 5. didn't, did not
6. isn't, is not 7. hadn't, had not
8. don't, do not 9. weren't, were not

Page 197
1. couldn't 2. wasn't 3. aren't
4. can't 5. don't 6. didn't
Sentences will vary.

Page 198
1. aren't 2. isn't 3. can't
4. haven't 5. don't 6. didn't
7. couldn't 8. weren't

Page 199
1. writes 2. meets 3. ride
4. shop 5. closes 6. forget
7. locks 8. bang 9. call 10. hear

Page 200
1. play 2. hides 3. chase 4. calls
5. run 6. stand 7. closes
8. nudges 9. sleeps 10. sleep

Page 201
1. make 2. cuts 3. use 4. glow
5. hang 6. buy 7. picks 8. picks
9. wear 10. sell

Page 202
1. camp 2. likes 3. walks 4. build
5. cook 6. crawl
Sentences will vary.

Page 203
1. plays 2. play 3. runs 4. run
5. dive 6. dives 7. climb
8. climbs 9. throw 10. throw

Page 204
1. brings 2. likes 3. trade 4. eat
5. drink 6. buy 7. asks
8. wants 9. puts 10. find

Page 205
1. had; past 2. had; past 3. has;
now 4. has; now 5. has; now
6. have; now 7. have; now
8. had; past

Page 206
1. has 2. have 3. had 4. have
5. has 6. had 7. had 8. have
9. has

Page 207
1. correct as is 2. has 3. had
4. had 5. has 6. have
7. correct as is 8. correct as is

Writing

Page 210
Many of; Our teacher; The reading;
The globe; We study; Our class

Page 211
1. Art class; 2. Today we;
3. First, we; 4. The next;
5. My teacher; 6. Next week

Page 212
1. The blue whale is the largest animal in the world. 2. Even dinosaurs were not as large as the blue whale. 3. Blue whales are not part of the fish family. 4. The blue whale has no teeth. 5. Blue whales eat tiny sea creatures. 6. Blue whales have two blowholes.

Page 213
Sentences will vary.

Page 214
1. Where is the king's castle?
2. Who helped Humpty Dumpty?
3. Why did the cow jump over the moon? 4. Will the frog become a prince? 5. Could the three mice see?

Page 215
Sentences will vary.

Page 216
1. .; 2. ?; 3. ?; 4. .; 5. ?; 6. .;
7. ?; 8. .

Page 217
1. The Sun is the closest star to Earth. 2. The Sun is not the brightest star. 3. What is the temperature of the Sun? 4. The Sun is a ball of hot gas. 5. How large is the Sun? 6. Will the Sun ever burn out?

Page 218
Sentences will vary.

Page 219
Dear Mom and Dad,
    Camp is so cool! Today we went swimming. Do you know what the best part of camp is? I think fishing is my favourite thing to do. Did you feed my hamster? I really miss you. Love, Dalton Sentences will vary.

Page 220
1. .; 2. ?; 3. !; 4. ?; 5. .; 6. !; 7. ?;
8. .; 9. ?; 10. !; 11. .; 12. ?

Page 221
Sentences will vary.

Page 222
Sentences will vary.

Page 223
Sentences will vary.

Page 224
Sentences may vary. Possible answers: 1. A boy climbs a tree in his backyard. 2. A cat plays with fish in the living room. 3. A bunny eats a carrot in the garden.

Page 225
Sentences and pictures will vary.

Page 226
Lists of words will vary.

Page 227
Answers will vary. 1. fat, three;
2. wooden, cold; 3. Orange, sunny;
4. lazy, muddy; 5. thirsty, shallow;
6. funny, black

Page 228
Describing words will vary.

Page 229
Sentences will vary.

Page 230
Sentences will vary.

Page 231
Sentences will vary.

Page 232
1. The party was fun and exciting.
2. We blew up orange and red balloons. 3. We ate cake and ice cream. 4. The cake frosting was green and yellow. 5. We made a bookmark and a clay pot. 6. We brought games and prizes.

Page 233
1. These peanuts and pretzels are salty. 2. The first graders and second graders eat lunch at noon. 3. Where is the salt and pepper? 4. The napkins and forks are on the table. 5. Are the muffins and cookies in the oven? 6. Mike and Ava bought lunch today.

Page 234
1. Fill a cup with water and add some flower seeds. 2. This will soften the seeds because they are hard. 3. Fill a cup with dirt while the seeds soak in water. 4. Bury the seeds in the cup until the dirt covers them. 5. Add water to the plant but do not add too much. 6. Set the cup in the sun so the plant will grow.

Page 235
Sentences will vary.

Page 236
Sentences will vary.

Page 237
Sentences will vary.

Page 238
Describing words will vary.
1. Sometimes I can see Mars, Jupiter, and Saturn with my telescope. 2. There are many stars in our galaxy. 3. Comets are large pieces of ice and rock. 4. The sun is really a huge star. 5. Is there life on any other planet? 6. Look at that beautiful shooting star! 7. Can you imagine traveling in space? 8. I think I saw a little alien.

Page 239
Describing words will vary.

Saturn is famous for the rings that surround it. Its rings are made of ice, rock, and dirt. The rings circle around the planet. Saturn is made of gas. Saturn's gases are lighter than water. That means Saturn would float if you put it into a tub of water. Saturn has a least 53 moons.

Page 240
1. took; 2. was; 3. saw; 4. many; 5. brought; 6. seen; 7. has; 8. are; 9. were; 10. saw; 11. wore; 12. going; 13. Does; 14. brought

Page 241
1. ~~brang~~, brought; 2. ~~seen~~, saw; 3. ~~gots~~, has; 4. ~~taked~~, took; 5. ~~is~~, are; 6. ~~runned~~, ran; 7. ~~got~~, have; 8. ~~was~~, were; 9. ~~saw~~, see; 10. ~~do~~, does; 11. ~~brang~~, brought; 12. ~~does~~, do

Page 242
Sentences will vary.

Page 243
Sentences will vary.

Page 244
Sentences will vary.

Page 245
Stories will vary.

Page 246
Sentences will vary.

Page 247
Sentences will vary.

Page 248
Sentences will vary.

Page 249
Answers will vary.

Page 250
Stories will vary.

Page 251
Stories will vary.

Maps

Page 254
1. yes 2. yes 3. yes 4. no
5. Answers will vary.

Page 255
3. They both show a place from above. 4. A photo has more detail.

Page 256
1. round 2. water 3. land where plants and trees grow

Page 257
1. round 2. smaller 3. the names of places

Pages 258–259
1. An x should be drawn on each continent 2. five 3.Africa, Antarctica, Asia, Australia
4. Atlantic, Arctic 5.A map is flat, but a globe is round.

Page 260
1. north 2. south 3. east 4. west

Page 261
1. Antarctica 2. Arctic Ocean
3. Indian Ocean: east; Europe: east and west; North America: west; Australia: east

Page 262
1. garden 2. south 3. west 4. ice skating rink

Page 263
1. east 2. north 3. west 4. south
5. apartment building

Page 264
Answers from left to right: 4, 6, 3, 2, 1, 5

Page 265
1. school 2. Clark Street 3. railroad
4. green 5. south

Pages 266–267
1. monkeys 2. east 3. yes 4. north
5. Circle Road 6. yes 7. no

Page 268
1. yes 2. no 3. no 4. no 5. yes
6. yes

Page 269
1. Jason 2. Buddy 3. Ellen 4. Mom
5. Buddy

Page 270
1. tennis court 2. B4 3. play golf
4. A2, B2, B1, C1

Page 271
1. B2 2. D2 3. A4 4. C4 5. C1
6. D4

Page 272
1. B1 2. a house 3. First Street
4. no 5. A3

Pages 273–274
1. A mountain is much higher than a plain. 2. a valley 3. possible answers: a bridge, a boat 4. a plain; because the land is flat 5. a mountain; because the land is steep
6. Answers will vary.

Page 275
1. ocean 2. swim, fish, sail 3. a river flows, a lake is surrounded by land

Page 276
Child should write answers on map.

Page 277
1. border 2. United States 3. south
4. Ottawa 5. west 6. Alaska
7. Rio Grande 8. Canada

Page 279

1. park 2. a book 3. south
4. Town hall 5. west 6. east
7. D1 8. First Street, Bell Avenue,
Second Street, Carol Street

Page 280

1. compass rose 2. map key
3. island 4. landforms
5. continent 6. mountain
Secret Message: Maps Are Fun

Addition & Subtraction

Page 284

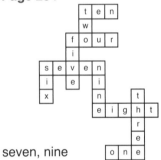

seven, nine

Page 285

Check that the child has drawn the
correct number of petals on each
flower. Bows with 4, 6, 8, and 10
should be coloured yellow. Bows with
3, 5, 7, and 9 should be coloured
purple.

Page 286

Page 287

A. 3, 2; B. 12, 5; C. 8, 6; D. 11, 7;
E. 7, 5; F. 12, 3; G. 4, 1; H. 10, 8; I. 9,
4; J. 11, 5; Answers will vary.

Page 288

Beans talk

$4 + 2 = 6$; $7 + 7 = 14$; $9 + 5 = 14$;
$10 + 4 = 14$; $4 + 8 = 12$; $6 + 8 = 14$;
$11 + 3 = 14$; $14 + 0 = 14$; $7 + 2 = 9$;
$13 + 1 = 14$; $5 + 8 = 13$; $12 + 2 =$
14; $7 + 4 = 11$; $5 + 9 = 14$

Page 289

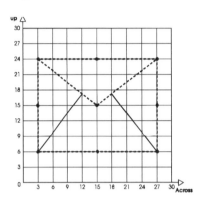

Page 290

21, 93, 78, 46, 44, 78; PLEASE
50, 67, 46, 79, 83, 59, 25, 66;
THANK YOU
59, 25, 66, 32, 78; YOU'RE
80, 78, 93, 18, 25, 35, 78;
WELCOME

Page 291

Answers will vary.

Page 292

38, 26, 97, 58, 67, 76, 79; 46, 84, 46,
89, 58, 48, 97; 58, 55, 65, 46, 40;
THREE-FOURTHS, PACIFIC

Page 293

23, 75, 99, 75, 47, 34, 75, 99, CANA-
DIAN; 85, 98, 33, 78, 63, 87, 32, 45,
78, 98; 65, 46, 55, 98, 88, 32, 21; 51,
86, 75, 64, FLAG

Page 294

1. $7 - 1 = 6$; 2. $9 - 2 = 7$;
3. $3 - 2 = 1$; 4. $8 - 4 = 4$;
5. $5 - 5 = 0$; 6. $6 - 1 = 5$;
7. $8 - 2 = 6$

The phone number is 671-4056.

Page 295

Page 296

Page 297

A bat

$5 - 2 = 3$; $7 - 7 = 0$; $18 - 9 = 9$; 17
$- 3 = 14$; $15 - 4 = 11$; $18 - 4 = 14$;
$12 - 3 = 9$; $11 - 9 = 2$; $16 - 9 = 7$;
$7 - 4 = 3$; $10 - 8 = 2$; $15 - 7 = 8$; $9 -$
$2 = 7$; $13 - 2 = 11$; $12 - 2 = 10$; 15
$- 2 = 13$; $9 - 6 = 3$; $6 - 6 = 0$; $9 - 7$
$= 2$; $15 - 9 = 6$; $16 - 8 = 8$;
$9 - 5 = 4$; $9 - 1 = 8$

Page 298

Page 299

68 - 26 = 42; 34 - 11 = 23; 91 - 20 = 71; 47 - 15 = 32; 67 - 13 = 54; 88 - 54 = 34; 19 - 12 = 7; 33 - 21 = 12; 69 - 59 = 10; 88 - 12 = 76; 28 - 24 = 4; 17 - 6 = 11; 57 - 55 = 2; 27 - 5 = 22; 97 - 13 = 84; 35 - 11 = 24; 81 - 21 = 60; 39 - 15 = 24; 60 - 10 = 50

Page 300

Page 301

62, 33, 23; 30, 21, 14; 61, 22, 41; The bird with the difference of 30 should be coloured red. The bird with the difference of 14 should be coloured blue. The birds with the differences of 22 and 33 should be coloured green.

Page 302

Page 303

54, 85, 43, 85; 43, 54, 67; 43, 67, 32; 32; Check child's colouring.

Page 304

10, 12, 16; 18, 14, 19; 15, 11, 17; Bowls with 11, 15, and 18 should be coloured yellow. Bowls with 10, 14, and 17 should be coloured pink. Bowls with 12, 16, and 18 should be coloured brown.

Page 305

Page 306

2 + 8 = 10; 24 + 7 = 31; 32 + 9 = 41; 1 + 9 = 10; 7 + 4 = 11; 45 + 5 = 50; 31 + 4 = 35; 11 + 9 = 20; 17 + 9 = 26; 22 + 13 = 35; 26 + 6 = 32; 19 + 9 = 28; 11 + 7 = 18; 16 + 22 = 38; 31 + 11 = 42; 14 + 9 = 23; 12 + 7 = 19; 40 + 14 = 54; 27 + 6 = 33; 12 + 9 = 21; 4 + 8 = 12; 41 + 21 = 62; 37 + 31 = 68; 16 + 6 = 22; 16 + 5 = 21; 10 + 24 = 34; 20 + 21 = 41; 15 + 5 = 20 Extra: Answers will vary.

Page 307

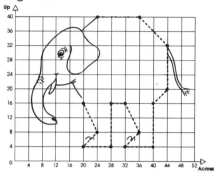

Page 308

A. 52, 93, 72, 93; B. 41, 62, 37, 37; C. 23, 50, 62, 62; D. 60, 32, 81, 60; E. 90, 44, 76, 44

Page 309

	71	93	90	52
92	90	91	86	92
81	81	73	42	92
85	74	92	90	94
51	41	93	81	

Page 310

Beach: Route #1—13 + 48 + 32 + 54 = 147 kilometres; Route #2—13 + 48 + 88 + 39 = 188 kilometres

Mountains: Route #1—13 + 17 + 31 + 49 = 110 kilometres; Route #2—13 + 28 + 10 + 25 = 76 kilometres

Page 311

1. 21; 2. 26; 3. 14; 4. 31 5. 35; 6. 28; 7. 27; 8. 29 9. 58; 10. 33

Page 312

15 + 33 + 27 = 75; 27 + 23 + 12 = 62; 34 + 23 + 24 = 81; 15 + 25 + 10 = 50; 16 + 14 + 14 = 44; 12 + 31 + 17 = 60; 28 + 22 + 45 = 95; 43 + 27 + 27 = 97; 10 + 17 + 18 = 45; 29 + 13 + 16 = 58; 37 + 31 + 17 = 85; 51 + 23 + 17 = 91

Page 313

35: 3 tens 5 ones, 2 tens 15 ones; 47: 4 tens 7 ones, 3 tens 17 ones; 82: 8 tens 2 ones, 7 tens 12 ones; 94: 9 tens 4 ones, 8 tens 14 ones; 61: 6 tens 1 one, 5 tens 11 ones; 90: 9 tens 0 ones, 8 tens 10 ones

Page 314

Boldfaced numbers should be circled.
A. **48**, 89; B. 79, **46**; C. 36, **76**; D. **77**, 59; E. **48**, 14; F. 61, **68**; G. 14, **39**; Answers will vary.

Page 315

A. 19, 39, 37; 1, 3, 2; B. 8, 6, 9; 2, 1, 3; C. 28, 37, 14; 2, 3, 1; D. 29, 38, 37; 1, 3, 2; E. 29, 36, 48; 1, 2, 3; F. 18, 15, 19; 2, 1, 3

Page 316

35 − 17 = 18; 62 − 28 = 34; 53 − 14 = 39; 92 − 27 = 65; 82 − 23 = 59; 83 − 28 = 55; 67 − 48 = 19; 58 − 29 = 29; 72 − 17 = 55; 73 − 58 = 15; 42 − 26 = 16; 90 − 81 = 9; 52 − 28 = 24; 56 − 19 = 37

Page 317

45 - 39 = 6; 84 - 59 = 25; 72 - 55 = 17; 71 - 19 = 52; 84 - 25 = 59; 60 - 18 = 42; 98 - 29 = 69; 74 - 15 = 59; 71 - 17 = 54; 88 - 29 = 59; 82 - 68 = 14; 91 - 32 = 59; 34 - 16 = 18; 92 - 13 = 79; 43 - 35 = 8; 57 - 28 = 29

She had 15 tickets left.

Page 318

65 − 27 = 38, 38 + 27 = 65; 77 − 38 = 39, 39 + 38 = 77; 24 − 15 = 9, 9 + 15 = 24; 32 − 13 = 19, 19 + 13 = 32; 83 − 49 = 34, 34 + 49 = 83; 50 − 19 = 31, 31 + 19 = 50; 46 − 29 = 17, 17 + 29 = 46; 62 − 15 = 47, 47 + 15 = 62

Answers will vary.

Page 319

U. 81; L. 5; N. 60; C. 46; O. 90; P. 38; H. 23; K. 63; S. 48; A. 14; G. 18; M. 71; R. 69; KANGAROO; KOALA; OPOSSUM; POUCH

Page 320

Check that the child has coloured the appropriate spaces. A. 21; B. 9; C. 26; D. 8; E. 13; F. 17; G. 30; H. 7

Page 321

A. 28 + 25 = 53; B. 25 − 9 = 16; C. 28 − 13 = 15; D. 12 + 9 = 21; E. 12 − 9 = 3; F. 13 + 28 = 41; G. 9 + 25 + 12 = 46; 98 students

Page 322

saw: 34 + 27 + 5 = 66; wrench: 48 + 36 + 15 = 99; hammer: 43 + 15

+ 27 = 85; pliers: 39 + 34 + 15 = 88; A. 27 + 15 = 42; B. 34 − 5 = 29, 48 − 15 = 33, 43 − 15 = 28; 39 − 15 = 24; 43 + 15 + 27 + 5 + 34 + 39 + 48 + 15 + 36 = 262

Page 323

2 hundreds 7 tens,
8 hundreds 4 tens,
9 hundreds 3 tens,
7 hundreds 1 ten;
5 hundreds 6 tens,
3 hundreds 2 tens,
4 hundreds 9 tens,
6 hundreds 5 tens; 570; 804

Page 324

Page 325

207 + 544 = 751; 126 + 89 = 215; 328 + 348 = 676; 257 + 458 = 715; 547 + 129 = 676; 624 + 127 = 751; 108 + 107 = 215; 229 + 418 = 647; 258 + 268 = 526; 379 + 336 = 715; 417 + 109 = 526; 153 + 494 = 647

Page 326

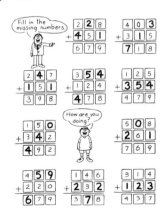

Page 327

A. $1.49 + $.50 + $.75 + $1.22 = $3.96; B. $1.72 + $.65 + $1.17 = $3.54; C. $1.86 + $1.84 + $.84 + $1.07 = $5.61; D. $1.53 + $1.90 + $1.22 + $.84 = $5.49; E. $1.86 + $.50 + $1.17 = $3.53; F. $1.49 + $.86 + $.75 = $3.10

Page 328

A. 123 + 406 + 406 = 935, orange; B. 209 + 81 + 147 + 181 + 72 = 690, green; C. 146 + 266 + 120 + 139 + 82 = 753, purple; D. 180 + 169 + 308 + 122 = 779, yellow; E. 154 + 154 + 188 + 93 + 82 + 170 = 841, red; F. 107 + 173 + 38 + 280 + 38 + 54 + 78 = 768, blue

Page 329

40 tens, 20 tens, 70 tens, 50 tens; 10 tens, 90 tens, 80 tens, 30 tens

Page 330

Page 331

900, 800, 700, 600, 500, 400, 300, 200, 100, Subtract 100.; 900, 700, 500, 300, 100, Subtract 200.; 800, 600, 400, 200, Subtract 200.

Page 332

66; 42; 203; 344; 213; 79; 469; 253; 234; 157; 129; 166; 309

Page 333

Check child's colouring.

Page 334

830; 438; 931; 239; 280; 733; 733; 736; 359; 759; 63; 338

Page 335

A. 700 − 523 = 177; B. 300 − 156 = 144; C. 248 + 176 = 424, 600 − 424 = 176; D. 189 + 96 = 285, 400 − 285 = 115; E. 398 + 275 = 673, 900 − 673 = 227

Page 336

A. 168 − 159 = 9; B. 427 + 289 = 716; C. 507 − 278 = 229; D. 319 + 299 = 618; E. 826 − 697 = 129; F. 258 + 273 = 531

Page 337

T. 500; O. 903; L. 285; P. 846; A. 535; W. 951; I. 870; P. 528; L. 979; I. 207; R. 821; I. 564; O. 254; A. 853; N. 273; N. 869; R. 517; H. 811; A. 894; LION, TAPIR, PIRANHA, OWL

Page 338

B. 773; E. 569; L. 467; H. 374; F. 248; D. 385; A. 796; N. 288; I. 834; O. 883; M. 689; C. 259; T. 896; R. 800; P. 704; FIREMAN, TEACHER, DOCTOR, LIBRARIAN, POLICEMAN

Page 339

sandals $2.10 + swimsuits $6.89 + sand toys $1.23 + swim ring $1.46 = $11.68

mittens $.77 + coat $7.14 + hat $1.23 + skis $3.74 = $12.88

$12.88 − $11.68 = $1.20

Page 340

Answers will vary.

Page 341

427 + 282 = 709, 636 − 550 = 86; 963 − 189 = 774, 148 + 370 = 518, 550 + 370 = 920, 804 − 636 = 168; 189 + 751 = 940, 579 − 282 = 297, 963 − 148 = 815, 415 + 189 = 604

Page 342

690; 199; 714; 237; 568; 477; 851; 901

Page 343

Game 1: 637, 616; 353, 454; 851, 800; 189, 326; 554, 820

Game 2: 283, 218; 412, 417; 536, 509; 844, 873; 172, 128

Math

Page 346

Page 347

A salamander

Page 348

1. 67; 2. 34, 35; 3. 42, 43; 4. 16, 18 5. 73, 74, 75; 6. 31, 32; 7. 10 12 14 16 8. 15 18 21 24; 9. 83, 84, 85, 86, 87, 88 10. after; 11. before; 12. after 13. before; 14. before; 15. before

Page 349

Students should follow these numbers:

13, 7, 3, 9, 19, 23, 11, 5, 17, 67, 33, 25, 27, 35, 39, 37, 23, 57, 47, 43, 21, 15, 39, 29

Page 350

Top side of the street: 50, 52, 54, 56
Bottom side of the street: 51, 53, 55

Extra: The even numbers are on one side of the street. The odd numbers are on the other side of the street.

Page 351

1. 11 < 21; 2. 56 < 72; 3. 47 = 47; 4. 64 >10 5. 59 = 59; 6. 38 >17; 7. 526 < 527; 8. 159 > 42 9–16. Answers will vary. 17. 73 61 54 37 18. 96 43 24 22; 19. 79 78 69 51 20. 51 37 27 15

Page 352

A sidewalk.   518, 315, 276, 693, 137, 564, 909, 811, 209, 717, 836, 321, 488, 857, 432, 707

Page 353

Page 354

This line could move up or down.   This line could move left or right.

Page 355

1. 32, 42, 52, 62, 72, 82, 92; 2. 70, 60, 50, 40, 30, 20, 10; 3. 67, 57, 47, 37, 27, 17, 7; 4. 44, 55, 66, 77, 88, 99

Page 356

Answers will vary.

Page 357

A. 1F, 2G, 3B, 4C or A, 5E, 6I, 7E, 8H, 9G, 10G, 11C B. 1B, 2F, 3D, 4I, 5F, 6E, 7A, 8D, 9I, 10F, 11I C. 1H, 2C, 3C, 4G, 5G, 6C, 7F, 8I, 9B, 10C or A, 11F

Page 358

1. 5; 2. 8; 3. 11; 4. 26; 5. 6 6. 10; 7. 12; 8. 16; 9. 18; 10. 24

What did the rocket say when it left the party? "Time to take off."

Page 359

1. 15; 2. 6; 3. 24; 4. 12; 5. 27 6. 18; 7. 30; 8. 36; 9. 33; 10. 0

What did the owl say when someone knocked on its door? "Whoooo is it?"

Page 360

4cm, 8cm; Two possible answers: 12 cm, because it grew 4 cm each week; or 16 cm, because it doubled in height each week

Page 361

10, 10, 10 Extra: 2

Page 362

3 groups: fish, shells, animals with multiple legs/arms

Page 363

Answers will vary.

Page 364

1. 4 + 5 = 9; 2. 11 - 6 = 5; 3. 9 + 7 = 16; 4. 4 + 8 = 12; 5. 3 - 2 = 1; 6. 7 + 7 = 14; 7. 15 - 10 = 5; 8. 2 + 8 = 10; 9. 5 - 2 = 3

Page 365

15; 8

Page 366

Extra: Answers will vary. Possible: Pepperoni is the most popular topping. Cheese is the next favourite topping. Sausage is the least favourite topping.

Page 367

1. 7:35, 35 minutes after 7, 25 minutes to 8; 2. 3:50, 50 minutes after 3, 10 minutes to 4 3. 9:15, 15 minutes after 9, 45 minutes to 10 4. 6:25, 25 minutes after 6, 35 minutes to 7; 5. 9:55, 55 minutes after 9, 5 minutes to 10 6. 2:05, 5 minutes after 2, 55 minutes to 3

Pages 368–369

1. Teeny Sandwiches; 75¢ 2. Donut Hole; 25¢ 3. Peanuts 4. Gulp of Juice 5. 95¢ 6. 50¢

Page 370

Alex's coins: 5¢ + 25¢ + 10¢ = 60¢ Billy's coins: 10¢ + 10¢ + 10¢ + 10¢ + 10¢ + 5¢ + 5¢ + 1¢ + 1¢ + 1¢ = 63¢ 63¢ > 60¢ Billy has more money.

Page 371

1. metres; 2. metres; 3. kilometres; 4. centimetres; 5. centimetres; 6. centimetres; 7. metres; 8. kilometres; 9. metres; 10. centimetres; 11. metres; 12. metres; 13. kilometres; 14. centimetres; 15. metres

Page 372

Sunny days: 12; Cloudy days: 8; Rainy days: 5; Snowy days: 6

Page 373

2.5 + 2.5 + 2.5 = 7.5 cm; 5 + 5 + 5 = 15 cm; 10 + 10 + 10 = 30 cm

Page 374

Page 375

Page 376

Answers will vary.

Page 377

2, size; Correct pies: 1, 3, 5

Page 378

1. 1/2; 2. 1/8; 3. 1/4; 4. 1/4; 5. 1/2; 6. 1/6 7. 1/2; 8. 1/2; 9. 3/4; 10. 1/4; 11. 1/2

Page 379

2/2 matches triangle, 2/3 matches circle, 2/12 matches rectangle; color 1/2 circle, color the whole rectangle

Page 380

1/5 of the circle, 4/5 of the rectangle, 3 ants, 2 spiders, 0 bees, 5 worms

Page 381

2/10, 6/10, 2/10, 6/10, 7/10